D1067872

LINEAR REGRESSION
AND ITS
APPLICATION TO ECONOMICS

LINEAR REGRESSION

AND ITS
APPLICATION TO ECONOMICS

BY

ZDZISŁAW HELLWIG

Translated from the Polish by
J. STADLER

Translation edited by
H. INFELD

PERGAMON PRESS

OXFORD · LONDON · NEW YORK · PARIS

PAŃSTWOWE WYDAWNICTWO EKONOMICZNE
WARSZAWA
1963

Library
I.U.P.
Indiana, Pa.

330.18   H369
c. 1

PERGAMON PRESS LTD.

Headington Hill Hall, Oxford

4 & 5 Fitzroy Square, London W. 1

PERGAMON PRESS INC.

122 East 55th Street, NEW YORK 22, N.Y.

GAUTHIER — VILLARS

55 Quai des Grands-Augustins, Paris 6

PERGAMON PRESS G. m. b. H.

Kaiserstrasse 75 Frankfurt am Main

Copyright © 1963

PERGAMON PRESS LTD.

Library of Congress Card Number 62–21781

Set by
Państwowe Wydawnictwo Ekonomiczne

Printed in Poland by
Drukarnia im. Rewolucji Październikowej

CONTENTS

INTRODUCTION

Increased interest in research methods employing *numbers* has been shown in economics in recent years. More and more tables, graphs and formulae are to be found in economic publications — in textbooks, monographs, articles and studies. Naturally the use of formal methematical methods of research must always be subordinate to qualitative analysis because of the complex character of socio-economic phenomena and processes. Economic research concentrates on the individual and social activities of *man* as an economic agent, on his behaviour as a producer or consumer, on his individual and social needs, on his customs, psychological reactions, tastes, likes and dislikes. Economics is one of the social sciences. It studies laws and relationships governing the social activities of men, particularly in the processes of production, distribution, exchange and consumption. Although in economic studies phenomena are primarily analysed in their qualitative aspects, it does not follow that their quantitative aspects may be neglected. Thus, for instance, economists analyse and attempt to explain the relationships between wages and the productivity of labour, costs and production, demand and price as well as personal income, the productivity of labour and the mechanization and automation of the production processes, national income and investment expenditures, etc. In order to provide information that is as complete as possible, an analysis of these relationships, besides explaining the mechanism, must enable us to *predict* the behaviour of one of the related phenomena when the behaviour of the others is known. This is usually impossible when the phenomena studied are not measurable and the relationships existing between them cannot be presented in functional form. In economic studies it can be seen at almost every step how closely interrelated are the qualitative and quantitative aspects of phenomena. *For this very reason a correct method of economic analysis cannot ignore the importance of the quantitative approach to the description and analysis of phenomena.*

Every day new and more specialized methods of research — using a more or less complex mathematical apparatus — are being adapted to economic studies. Usually they are statistical methods[1], but because of the sphere of their application they are generally referred to as *econometric* methods. A very great progress has been made recently in econometric research and many interesting books dealing with econometrics have been published. These books contain ample evidence that the most valuable statistical methods applicable to economic analysis are those belonging to the theory of correlation and regression.

In economic applications of regression theory, linear regression is of greatest importance. This is for many reasons, of which the most important are:

1) linear regression is a simpler concept than curvilinear regression and the calculations involved are much less complicated;

2) linear regression appears most frequently in practice; as is well known, the regression lines in a two-dimensional normal distribution are straight lines; therefore, in studying two-dimensional populations we deal with

---

[1] Seldom mathematical in the narrow sense of this word. An example of a mathematical method may be found in analysis of inter-branch flows (or input–output analysis), or in programming (linear, non-linear, dynamic).

linear regression at least as often as with a *normal distribution*. An explanation of why a normal distribution appears frequently is, in turn, found in the Central Limit Theorem;

3) curvilinear regression can often be replaced by linear regression which provides an approximation close enough for practical purposes;

4) curvilinear regression may be reduced to linear regression by replacing the curve by linear segments;

5) linear regression is of particular importance for multi-dimensional variables. It is known that the nature of a function approximating regression I may be inferred from a scatter diagram. When the number of variables is greater than three a diagram cannot be drawn and common sense indicates that linear regression (being the simplest) should be used in such cases.

This book has been written primarily for scientists in economic, agricultural and technical colleges who deal with economic problems in their research. It is also addressed to graduates of economic and technical colleges employed in different branches of the national economy who — because of their occupation — have frequent occasion to use statistical methods in studying the relationships between phenomena. To this group belong primarily those engaged in planning, statistics, cost accounting, economic analysis, time and motion studies, inventory control, and technology. This book may also be of some help to students in day and correspondence courses run by schools of economics and business. In order to use it with ease it is necessary to have a basic knowledge of calculus and of some elements of the theory of probability and mathematical statistics. Since economists are usually interested in the humanities and their knowledge of mathematics is often rather scanty, the outline of this book is so designed as to facilitate its use by enabling the reader to omit the more difficult parts without interfering with his understanding of the whole exposition. Those parts that require a better knowledge of mathematics and statistics are marked with one asterisk (*) at the beginning and with two (**) at the end. They may be omitted without lessening the understanding of the main ideas behind the methods presented, or the mastering of the computation technique. If the more difficult parts are omitted this book is accessible even to those whose background in mathematics and statistics is quite modest, so that the circle of its readers may be quite wide. Even though they will not be able to learn about all the more formal aspects of statistical research methods and of descriptions of relationships existing among phenomena which are presented in this book, they can learn the *intuitive and computational aspects* of these methods. This, of course, is most important from the point of view of the wide dissemination of the methods presented.

The book has been divided into 6 chapters.

Chapter 1 constitutes the background for the whole work. It comprises the elementary concepts and the more important definitions and theorems concerning two-dimensional and multi-dimensional random variables. This chapter also contains an explanation of the symbols and terms used in the book. In Chapter 2 the more important applications of correlation methods to economics are reviewed. So far, correlation methods have rarely been used in economic analysis. The review of applications given in Chapter 2 and numerous examples quoted in the following chapters will illustrate the usefulness of statistical methods in analysing the relationships among random variables.

In Chapter 3 methods of estimating regression parameters are discussed. Chapter 4 deals with methods of testing some statistical hypotheses important for practical applications of the correlation analysis. Particularly worth noting are non-parametric tests for verifying the hypothesis that the two-dimensional population is normal, and non-parametric test for verifying the hypothesis that the regression in the population is a linear regression. In Chapter 5 methods of transformation of curvilinear regression into linear regression are discussed. In examples illustrating the computational technique of determining regression parameters a new method called the two-point method has been used. In the last Chapter (6) an attempt has been made at a new approach to the problem of trend. It is known that the determination of trend parameters, in a formal sense, does not differ from the determination of regression parameters. There are, however, differences of substance between the trend line and the regression line, and, therefore, it is necessary to define the trend line in a way different from the definition of the regression line. This definition is given in Chapter 6, which is also a concluding chapter, in order to emphasize the fact that correlation methods can be used not only in static but also in dynamic research.

This work deals with two-dimensional variables. Most of the results obtained, however, may be generalized and applied to multi-dimensional variables. The author has tried to use diverse types of statistical data so as to create a broad basis for checking the usefulness of the two-point method he proposes for determining regression line parameters. For this reason, the work contains not only the results of the author's own research, but also statistical data from the works of other authors. Figures in rectangular brackets [ ] denote the numbers of the items in the Bibliography. Statistical data used in the book are quoted either in the text or in the Appendix at the end of the book.

The work is divided into chapters, sections and items. The decimal system is used in denoting them. The first figure denotes the chapter, the second — the section, and the third — the item. Thus, 2.2.3. denotes the third item of the second section of the second chapter.

Formulae, tables and graphs are numbered separately for each numbered part of the book.

1. REGRESSION AND CORRELATION

1.1. General comments on regression and correlation

It is commonly known that one of the basic elements of the learning process is the scientific experiment. However, there are sciences in which it is very difficult to experiment, especially if the word *experiment* is understood to mean studying the object in question under conditions *artificially created* for this purpose. To this category belong, primarily, the social sciences, and among them — again in first place — economics interpreted in the broad sense of the word (i.e. not only political economy, but also all the related economic disciplines).

In those sciences in which experimenting is difficult or impossible, the process of learning is particularly cumbersome. One of the objectives of an experiment is to establish a causal relation between the phenomenon studied and other phenomena. To achieve this purpose a large number of experiments have to be carried out and in the process the influence of those factors ₎which may be related to the phenomenon studied is gradually eliminated and observations regarding the behaviour of the phenomenon are made in isolation.

In this way experimenting may help in recognizing which factors exert an essential influence on the behaviour of the phenomenon studied, and which affect it slightly, non-essentially or not at all. If, for any reason, experimenting is impossible (e.g. when it creates a danger to human life, or is too costly, or technically impossible) then the process of learning must take its course under natural conditions. In such cases the search for a causal relation between the phenomenon studied and its environment is particularly difficult because then the question arises how to classify the phenomena into those which essentially affect the behaviour of the phenomenon studied and those with negligible influence. The answer to this question is provided by statistics. *The importance of statistical methods of analysis is of the highest order for those sciences in which it is difficult to experiment*, even if these sciences are as widely separated as demography and quantum physics.

Suppose that we are interested in two phenomena, A and B. We have to find out whether or not one affects the other. If both phenomena can be expressed numerically then for the description of their mutual relationship we may use the mathematical apparatus provided by the theory of function. Such sciences as physics and mechanics very often make use of mathematical functions to describe the relationship existing between two phenomena. The quantities with which these sciences deal may be considered as ordinary mathematical variables. Thus, for instance, distance travelled is a function of time and speed; voltage is a function of current intensity and resistance; work is a function of power and distance.

Besides phenomena which have a relationship so close that it may be regarded, for practical purposes, as functional, there are others among which the relationship is weak and obscured by the impact of many other forces of a secondary nature which cannot be eliminated while making observations. This type of relationship occurs when there exists an interdependence between random variables. We say that *two random variables are stochastically dependent* (as distinct from functionally) *if a change in one of them causes a change in the distribution of the other* (see [16], p. 364).

Example 1. We are interested in the problem of the effect of nutrition on the length of human life. The *scatter diagram*

GRAPH 1.

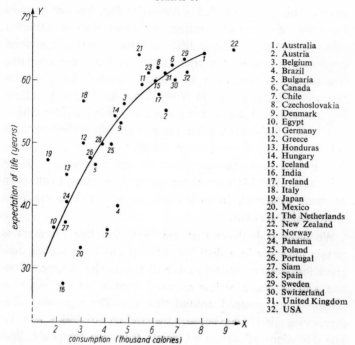

1. Australia
2. Austria
3. Belgium
4. Brazil
5. Bulgaria
6. Canada
7. Chile
8. Czechoslovakia
9. Denmark
10. Egypt
11. Germany
12. Greece
13. Honduras
14. Hungary
15. Iceland
16. India
17. Ireland
18. Italy
19. Japan
20. Mexico
21. The Netherlands
22. New Zealand
23. Norway
24. Panama
25. Poland
26. Portugal
27. Siam
28. Spain
29. Sweden
30. Switzerland
31. United Kingdom
32. USA

Note. The calories in the table above are "vegetable calories" in which an allowance is made for a higher value in calories obtained from proteins.

is shown on Graph 1. The x-axis represents average food consumption per person, measured in calories, and the y-axis — expectation of life of man. On the graph we see a collection of points. Each point may be regarded as a realization (x, y) of a two-dimensional random variable (X, Y) where X denotes the consumption of food and Y the expectation of life of man. The points are numbered. On the right side of the graph there is a list of countries, all numbered for easy identification of the points corresponding to particular countries. The distribution of the points on the graph shows a clear tendency. It is expressed by a curve drawn among the points. This curve is called a *regression line*. The ordinates of the curve give the expectation of life of man in different countries corresponding to different values of the average food consumption in those countries. It follows that a regression line is a functional expression of a stochastic relationship between random variables X and Y. If the regression line is a straight line we call it a *linear* regression. Its practical importance is of a very high order. When the relationship studied pertains not to two, but to a greater number of random variables, then instead of a regression line we get a *regression plane* (with three variables) or a *regression hyperplane* (with four or more variables). In such cases we deal with a multi-dimensional regression.

We have said above that the regression line expresses a certain tendency in a distribution of points on a scatter diagram. Particular points (x, y), as a rule, do *not* lie on a regression line, and are more or less removed from it but the *majority* of points are grouped around this line. The regression line expresses a relationship between the random variables Y and X. The deviations of particular points from the regression line may be considered a result of the influence of a variety of random factors. Let us imagine that a study of the interdependence between the length of human life and the consumption of food may be carried out under conditions ensuring the *absolute* elimination of the influence of any other factors besides food consumption on the length of life. (In practice, of course, this is impossible.) It could be surmised that under such circumstances the points on the graph would lie almost exactly along a certain curve which would mean that the relationship between variables Y and X is functional and not stochastic. It might be expected that the shape of such a curve would approximate the shape of the regression curve shown on Graph 1.

The importance of the regression line as a tool of learning consists in the fact that it permits us to relate to any value of one variable the *expected* or *most probable* value of the other variable. This is of particular importance in cases *when accurate observation of the values of one of the variables encounters substantial difficulties.* Let us suppose, for instance, that we want to estimate the amount of timber that can be obtained from 1,000 hectares of forest. If we know the regression line describing the relationship between the amount of timber in a tree trunk and the circumference of the trunk measured at a certain height, we can easily solve the problem.

The regression line is a tool of scientific prediction; if we know the value of one variable the regression line allows us to estimate the corresponding value of the other variable. The less the particular points deviate from the regression line, the better and the more accurate will be our estimate, because then a stochastic relationship is transformed into a functional relationship. The influence of random factors disappears and that of a regular factor is revealed more clearly. The bond between the two variables studied becomes stronger.

The whole group of problems related to *measuring the strength of the relationship between random variables* is the subject of the branch of statistics called *correlation theory*[1]. The measures of correlation most frequently used are: *the correlation coefficient and the correlation ratio.*

Statistical methods of studying interdependence between random variables allow us not only to measure the strength of this interdependence but also to verify the hypothesis that two variables are correlated with one another. The objective of every science is to discover and to explain causal relations existing between phenomena. Sometimes such relations are

---

[1] The word "correlation" in statistics means interdependence between random variables.

strong and immediately apparent. Often, however, they are weak and hidden among many diverse relationships existing between the phenomenon studied and the outside world. The researcher, on the basis of his scientific analysis, assumes the hypothesis that there exists a causal relationship between two defined phenomena. It may happen that it is impossible to test this hypothesis by a direct experiment. Correlation theory has at its disposal methods which allow us, in many cases, to verify such hypotheses.

Example 2. The hypothesis has been postulated that an increase in the consumption of animal protein reduces fertility. This hypothesis seems to be fairly unexpected. It cannot be tested by experimenting. Its verification, however, can be carried out on the basis of statistical data contained in Table 1

TABLE 1

THE RELATIONSHIP BETWEEN THE BIRTH RATE
AND CONSUMPTION OF PROTEIN

No	Country	Birth rate per thousand	Daily consumption of animal protein in grammes per person
1	Formosa	45·6	4·7
2	Malaya	39·7	7·5
3	India	33·0	8·7
4	Japan	27·0	9·7
5	Yugoslawia	25·9	11·2
6	Greece	23·5	15·2
7	Italy	23·4	15·2
8	Bulgaria	22·2	16·8
9	Germany	20 0	37·3
10	Ireland	19·1	46·7
11	Denmark	18·3	59·1
12	Australia	18·0	59·9
13	USA	17·9	61·4
14	Sweden	15·0	61·6

(see [5], p. 82). Even a casual glance at the data contained in this table indicates that the birth rate decreases as the consumption of animal protein increases. We are dealing here with a case of *negative correlation*. This term is used to define the type of correlation in which an increase in the value of one random variable is accompanied by a decrease in the value of the other. The relationship between the birth rate and the consumption of animal protein becomes even more

GRAPH 2.

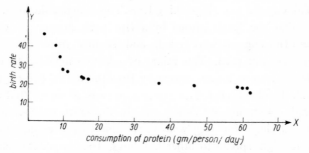

apparent on a scatter diagram (Graph 2). The trend in the distribution of the points on the graph is very distinctly marked. Of course, neither the table nor the graph provides a basis for accepting the hypothesis.

Methods for testing hypotheses of this kind will be discussed later. We shall here, however, take the opportunity to say a few words about *apparent or spurious correlation*. This is the type of correlation in which a relationship appears between statistical series, but there is no causal relation between the phenomena described by these series. For instance, let phenomenon A be causally related to phenomenon B and phenomenon C. There will be a correlation between the statistical series describing A and the series describing B. The same situation will exist with regard to C which will show correlation with A. It is clear that owing to the correlation between the series describing A and B and the correlation between the series describing

A and *C*, there may also appear a correlation between the series describing *B* and *C*. However, this type of relationship between statistical series is of a formal mathematical nature, since there is no direct causal relation between *B* and *C*.

Statistical experience supplies many illustrations of spurious relationships. For example Tschuprow [59] states that the statistics on compulsory fire insurance in prewar Russia showed an unusually close relationship between the average number of buildings destroyed in one fire and the application of fire engines to extinguishing fires. The evidence shows therefore that the losses caused by a fire were greater in cases where fire engines were used, and smaller in cases where they were not used. This might be taken to indicate that in order to reduce losses caused by fires the use of fire engines should be abandoned. The explanation was of course that fire brigades were usually called only in the more serious cases. When a single building was on fire and there was no danger that it might spread to other buildings, fire brigades usually did not interfere. In this case, then, there is an interdependence between the intensity of a fire and the participation of a fire brigade which uses fire engines. There is no causal relationship, however, between the application of fire engines and the number of buildings destroyed. This is an example of a spurious relationship.

In prewar Russian statistics we find further interesting examples of spurious relationships. For instance, it has been established on the basis of abundant statistical material that when a doctor assisted in child birth, the percentage of still-born children was higher than in cases delivered by a mid-wife. At first glance it might appear that in order to reduce infant mortality, doctors should not be called, a conclusion which is obviously absurd.

It turns out that the relationship observed is a spurious relationship. It should be remembered that formerly the doctor was called at childbirth only in serious cases which often ended in the death of the infant. Hence the numerical relationship between infant mortality and the assistance of qualified medical personnel.

The relationship between a drop in crop yields and the number of fires, observed by statisticians, also belongs to the category of spurious correlations. The number of fires increased in the years when precipitation was low. In the same years yields were lower than average.

An amusing case of spurious correlation between the number of registered births and the number of storks has been noted in Scandinavian countries on the basis of abundant statistical data.

The above examples of spurious correlation prove that *categorical judgments about the existence of causal relations should not be formed* on the basis of numerical relationships. A causal relation *may* exist but *does not* necessarily *exist*. When there is a causal relation between observed phenomena it may be expected that there will also be a numerical relationship. This relationship may sometimes appear very distinctly and sometimes less distinctly, or it may be so weak that it will hardly be noticeable. Such a relationship exists, however, when there is a causal relation between the phenomena studied.

Inferring that there is a causal relation on the basis of a numerical interdependence may lead to an absurd conclusion, as we have seen from the above examples. Their very absurdity protects us from accepting them. However, if the conclusions resulting from a hypothesis based on mathematical premises that a causal relation exists between phenomena are not absurd then the temptation to accept them may be very strong. One must not yield to such temptations. If there is a relationship between two statistical series the following cases are possible:

1) there is a causal relation between the phenomena described by these series;

2) there is no direct causal relation between the phenomena described by these series because they are correlated with *another, unknown* series describing a phenomenon causally related to the phenomena studied by us;

3) the observed relationship is accidental.

Choosing the first possibility would be tantamount to giving it priority over the remaining two without any foundation. The mere existence of a correlation between statistical series is only a signal that there may exist some direct or indirect relation between the phenomena described by these series.

Summing up, we may formulate the following rules:

1) *if a causal relation has been discovered* between two phenomena then correlation analysis may be used to determine the strength of this relation;

2) if a causal relation *has not been discovered*, but it may be assumed that such a relation between the studied phenomena does exist, then the appearance of a distinct correlation on the basis of more abundant statistical material substantially strengthens the hypothesis that a causal relation exists;

3) finally, if *before making observations there were no grounds for postulating a relationship* between two phenomena, but *after observations have been completed* and statistical material compiled *a distinct correlation between statistical series can be noticed*, then there is reason to assume that a causal relation may exist between the phenomena studied. It follows that even a formal analysis of a numerical relationship is fully justified since it may lead to a scientific discovery.

The usefulness of the rules formulated above becomes particularly apparent in Example 2, where we deal with a very strong interdependence between two statistical series: between the series on the birth rate in different countries and the series on the daily consumption of animal protein in those countries. In spite of a strong correlation between these series it should not be inferred on this basis that there exists a causal relation between fertility and the consumption of animal protein. Various sciences are engaged in discovering and explaining causal relations. Statistics facilitates these tasks for them by supplying useful research tools.

In economic research, regression analysis and correlation analysis find very many applications. In company economics or in "micro-economics", the whole cost and effectiveness theory has been worked out for industrial enterprises[1] on the basis of regression analysis. Amongst studies in this field the following should be named: [9], [12], [13], [18], [19], [23], [37], [49], [57]. Correlation analysis can also be applied in the economics of the firm to the analysis of the velocity of circulation of liquid assets, to studies on the productivity of labour and the degree of utilization of working time, to the analysis of wages and the wage fund, etc. A separate field for the application of correlation methods is that of the technology of production. Correlation analysis and particularly regression analysis can be of great service in studying the influence of technological processes on the quality and cost of the product and on the length of the production period.

In macro-economic studies correlation is used primarily for determining Engel curves and supply and demand curves. There are many works in this field. We shall mention here only some of the more important: [3], [22], [36], [39], [45], [46], [50], [51], [60].

---

[1] Since the author has been engaged so far in studying the applications of linear regression primarily to the analysis of the effectiveness of the industrial enterprise, most of the examples quoted in the book are from this field of research. The book also contains examples of other applications, since the author is interested in demonstrating by many and diversified examples the usefulness of the two-point method proposed by him for the determination of regression parameters.

An important and now widely studied statistical problem is the application of correlation methods to the analysis of time series (the determination of the trend, the analysis of seasonal factors, the auto-correlation of time series, correlograms). Among the more important works the following should be mentioned: [9], [33], [62].

1.2. Two-dimensional random variables[1]

1.2.1. Definitions and symbols

Let D be a given set of events forming a complete group (see [25], p. 22). If a pair of numbers has been assigned to each of the events, these numbers may be treated as the values of two functions determined on the set D.

Definition 1. A pair of functions of real variables determined on the set D is called a two-dimensional random variable. Two-dimensional variables are usually denoted by the symbol

$$\xi = (X_1, X_2). \tag{1}$$

Definition 1 can easily be generalized to include multi-dimensional variables. In addition to notation (1) a two-dimensional variable may also be denoted as follows:

$$\xi = (X, Y). \tag{2}$$

In this work we shall use only notation (2). Multi-dimensional variables are generally denoted by

$$\xi = (X_1, X_2, ..., X_n). \tag{3}$$

Random variables are sometimes interpreted geometrically. To each event from set D a certain arbitrary point on the plane correspond so that the set of events D has a corresponding set of points D' on the plane. The location of points on

---

[1] Items 1.2.1., 1.2.2. and 1.2.3. have been published in paper [29].

the two-dimensional plane R_2 is determined by two components. These components of the points of set D' are *the two-dimensional random variable* $\xi = (X, Y)$.

An equivalent of a random variable in statistics is a statistical characteristic. A population with two characteristics is called *a two-dimensional population*. Two characteristics of a population are equivalent to a two-dimensional random variable and *particular statistical observations* expressing the values of each of these characteristics for particular statistical units belonging to the population analysed are equivalents of the realization of the two-dimensional random variable. An example of a two-dimensional population is the labour force of a factory studied from the point of view of seniority in employment and earnings.

Similarly, as in the case of one-dimensional random variables, two-dimensional random variables may be treated as *discrete random variables and continuous random variables*.

1.2.2. *Two-dimensional discrete random variables*

Definition 1. The two-dimensional random variable (X,Y) is a discrete variable if the sets of values of variable X and variable Y are finite or denumerable.

Definition 2. The distribution function of the two-dimensional random variable is a function which assigns appropriate probabilities to the values of this variable. The distribution function of the two-dimensional discrete random variable is expressed in the following way:

$$P(X = x_i, Y = y_j) = p_{ij}. \tag{1}$$

If a set of values of the variable is finite then these values and the probabilities corresponding to particular values of the variable can be set out in the following contingency table:

TABLE 1

CONTINGENCY TABLE

X \ Y	y_1	y_2	$\cdots$	y_j	$\cdots$	y_n	$\underset{j}{\Sigma}$
x_1	p_{11}	p_{12}	$\cdots$	p_{1j}	$\cdots$	p_{1n}	$p_{1\cdot}$
x_2	p_{21}	p_{22}	$\cdots$	p_{2j}	$\cdots$	p_{2n}	$p_{2\cdot}$
:	:	:	: : :	:	: : :	:	:
x_i	p_{i1}	p_{i2}	$\cdots$	p_{ij}	$\cdots$	p_{in}	$p_{i\cdot}$
:	:	:	: : :	:	: : :	:	:
x_m	p_{m1}	p_{m2}	$\cdots$	p_{mj}	$\cdots$	p_{mn}	$p_{m\cdot}$
$\underset{i}{\Sigma}$	$p_{\cdot 1}$	$p_{\cdot 2}$	$\cdots$	$p_{\cdot j}$	$\cdots$	$p_{\cdot n}$	1

Since a set of events which determines the two-dimensional random variable forms a complete group of events, then

$$\sum_{i=1}^{m} \sum_{j=1}^{n} p_{ij} = 1. \tag{2}$$

Sum (2) is obtained by adding together all the probabilities contained in Table 1. This can be done in two ways: by summing up the rows and then the sums of the rows in the last column, or the other way around, by summing up the columns and then the sums of the columns in the last row. It follows that the sum of the last column equals the sum of the last row and equals one, i.e.

$$\sum_{i=1}^{m} p_{i\cdot} = 1, \tag{3}$$

$$\sum_{j=1}^{n} p_{\cdot j} = 1, \tag{4}$$

where

$$p_{i.} = \sum_{j=1}^{n} p_{ij}, \qquad (5)$$

$$p_{.j} = \sum_{i=1}^{m} p_{ij}. \qquad (6)$$

It follows from equations (3) and (4) that the probabilities shown in the last colun n and in the last row of Table 1 form distributions. They are called *marginal distributions* of the discrete random variable (X, Y).

Let us write the sum on the right side of formula (5) in a developed form:

$$p_{i.} = p_{i1} + p_{i2} + ... + p_{in}. \qquad (7)$$

After dividing both sides of equation (7) by $p_{i.}$ we get

$$\frac{p_{i1}}{p_{i.}} + \frac{p_{i2}}{p_{i.}} + ... + \frac{p_{in}}{p_{i.}} = 1. \qquad (8)$$

Since sum (8) equals unity then we have a probability distribution. It is *the conditional distribution of Y on X*. Let us denote

$$p(y_j \,|\, x_i) = \frac{p_{ij}}{p_{i.}}, \qquad p(x_i \,|\, y_j) = \frac{p_{ij}}{p_{.j}}, \qquad (9)$$

where $p(y_j|x_i)$ is the conditional probability that $Y = y_j$, based on the assumption that $X = x_i$, and $p(x_i|y_j)$ is the conditional probability that $X = x_i$, assuming that $Y = y_j$. Therefore, formula (8) may be written in the following short form:

$$\sum_{j=1}^{n} p(y_j \,|\, x_i) = 1. \qquad (10)$$

Similarly the conditional distribution of X on Y may be presented in the following form:

$$\sum_{i=1}^{m} p(x_i \mid y_j) = 1. \tag{11}$$

On the basis of (9)

$$p_{ij} = p_{i.} \cdot p(y_j \mid x_i) = p_{.j} \cdot p(x_i \mid y_j). \tag{12}$$

It follows from formula (12) that the *two-dimensional joint probability equals the product of the marginal probability of one variable and the conditional probability of the other.* The term "joint probability" is denoted by p_{ij}. This emphasizes the fact that p_{ij} is the probability of a two-dimensional variable, whereas $p_{i.}$, $p_{.j}$, $p(x_i|y_j)$, $p(y_j|x_i)$ are the probabilities of one-dimensional variables.

Definition 3. Two *discrete random variables X and Y are independent* if for all i, j

$$p(y_j \mid x_i) = p_{.j} \tag{13}$$

or, what amounts to the same thing:

$$p(x_i \mid y_j) = p_{i.}. \tag{14}$$

In this case formula (12) assumes a simpler form:

$$p_{ij} = p_{i.} \cdot p_{.j}. \tag{15}$$

Hence it follows on the basis of (12), (13) and (14) that for $r \leqslant m$, $s \leqslant n$ the following equality holds:

$$\sum_{i=1}^{r} \sum_{j=1}^{s} p_{ij} = \sum_{i=1}^{r} p_{i.} \sum_{j=1}^{s} p(y_j \mid x_i)$$

$$= \sum_{j=1}^{s} p_{.j} \sum_{i=1}^{r} p(x_i \mid y_j) \tag{16}$$

and finally

$$\sum_{i=1}^{r} \sum_{j=1}^{s} p_{ij} = \sum_{i=1}^{r} p_{i.} \sum_{j=1}^{s} p_{.j}. \tag{17}$$

Definition 4. Function $F(x, y) = P(X < x, Y < y)$ is called a two-dimensional distribution function of random variable (X,Y)[1].

When the two-dimensional random variable is discrete then it follows from the definition of the distribution function that

$$F(x, y) = \sum_{x_i < x} \sum_{y_j < y} p_{ij} \tag{18}$$

and

$$F(+\infty, +\infty) = \sum_{x_i < \infty} \sum_{y_j < \infty} p_{ij} = 1. \tag{19}$$

The marginal distribution of variable X is expressed by the formula

$$F(x, +\infty) = \sum_{x_i < x} \sum_{y_j < \infty} p_{ij} \tag{20}$$

or

$$F(x, +\infty) = \sum_{x_i < x} p_i.$$

The formulae for the marginal distribution of variable Y are analogous:

$$F(+\infty, y) = \sum_{x_i < \infty} \sum_{y_j < y} p_{ij.} = \sum_{y_j < y} p_{.j}. \tag{21}$$

It follows from formulae (17), (20) and (21) that if two discrete random variables X and Y are independent the two-dimensional distribution function (X,Y) is equal to the product of the distribution functions of one-dimensional variables X and Y. The reverse statement is also true.

---

[1] The definition of one-dimensional distribution function is analogous. The distribution function of x is function $F(x) = P(X < x)$.

1.2.3. Two-dimensional continuous random variables

Definition 1. The density function $f(x,y)$ of the two-dimensional random variable (X,Y) is a mixed derivative of second order of the distribution function $F(x,y)$ with respect to x and y of this variable at point (x,y), i.e.

$$f(x, y) = \frac{\partial^2 F}{\partial x \partial y}. \tag{1}$$

Definition 2. The two-dimensional random variable (X,Y) is continuous if its distribution function $F(x,y)$ is continuous and if the density function $f(x,y)$ is also a continuous function with the possible exception of a collection of points belonging to a finite number of curves.

On the basis of Definition 1 we have:

$$F(x, y) = \int\limits_{-\infty}^{x} \int\limits_{-\infty}^{y} f(u, v) du\, dv \tag{2}$$

and

$$F(+\infty, +\infty) = \int\limits_{-\infty}^{\infty} \int\limits_{-\infty}^{\infty} f(u, v) du\, dv = 1, \tag{3}$$

$$F(-\infty, -\infty) = F(-\infty, y) = F(x, -\infty) = 0. \tag{4}$$

The marginal distribution of variable X is expressed by the formula

$$F(x, \infty) = \int\limits_{-\infty}^{x} \int\limits_{-\infty}^{\infty} f(u, v)\, du\, dv = \int\limits_{-\infty}^{x} f_1(u) du. \tag{5}$$

In formula (5)

$$f_1(x) = \int\limits_{-\infty}^{\infty} f(x, y)\, dy \tag{6}$$

denotes the marginal density of variable X.

The formulae for the distribution function and marginal density of variable Y are analogous owing to the symmetry of the formulae. We shall denote the marginal distribution functions of variables X and Y by $F_1(x)$ and $F_2(y)$.

In discussing the two-dimensional discrete random variable we have given the definition of conditional probability (p. 15, formula (9)).

When the random variable is continuous, we shall understand the conditional probability

$$P(y \leqslant Y < y + \Delta_y \mid x \leqslant X < x + \Delta_x)$$

as the expression

$$P(y \leqslant Y < y + \Delta_y \mid x \leqslant X < x + \Delta_x)$$
$$= \frac{P(y \leqslant Y < y + \Delta_y, \, x \leqslant X < x + \Delta_x)}{P(x \leqslant X < x + \Delta_x)} \qquad (7)$$

assuming at the same time that $P(x \leqslant X < x + \Delta_x) > 0$. Comparing formula (7) with formula (9) from the preceding section we can easily notice a formal similarity between them. Indeed, in formula (7), instead of quantities x_i and y_j we have put in expressions $(x \leqslant X < x + \Delta_x)$ and $(y \leqslant Y < y + \Delta_y)$, respectively. For continuous random variables, probabilities corresponding to particular values of the variables always equal zero, since we have

$$P(X = x) = P(Y = y) = P(X = x, Y = y) = 0.$$

Conditional probability (7) is the probability that point (X, Y), chosen at random, will be located in rectangle

GRAPH 1.

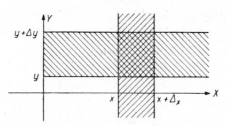

$y \leqslant Y < y + \Delta_y$, $x \leqslant X < x + \Delta_x$ when it is known that this point lies within area $x \leqslant X < x + \Delta_x$, $-\infty < Y < \infty$ (Graph 1).

It follows from the definition of the distribution function of the continuous variable that

$$P(y \leqslant Y < y + \Delta_y \mid x \leqslant X < x + \Delta_x)$$

$$= \frac{\int\limits_{x}^{x+\Delta_x} \int\limits_{y}^{y+\Delta_y} f(u, v) \, du \, dv}{\int\limits_{x}^{x+\Delta_x} \int\limits_{-\infty}^{\infty} f(u, v) \, du \, dv}. \tag{8}$$

Of course

$$P(-\infty < Y < \infty \mid x \leqslant X < x + \Delta_x) = 1. \tag{9}$$

The conditional distribution function is expressed by the formula

$$P(Y < y \mid x \leqslant X < x + \Delta_x)$$

$$= \frac{\int\limits_{x}^{x+\Delta_x} \int\limits_{-\infty}^{y} f(u, v) \, du \, dv}{\int\limits_{x}^{x+\Delta_x} \int\limits_{-\infty}^{\infty} f(u, v) \, du \, dv}, \tag{10}$$

and the density $f(y|x)$ of the conditional distribution by formula

$$f(y \mid x) = \frac{f(x, y)}{f_1(x)}. \tag{11}$$

In formulating the definition of conditional probability (see formula (7)) we considered variable Y on the assumption that variable X satisfies the inequality $x \leqslant X < x + \Delta_x$.

It is easy to find formulae for variable X which are symmetrical to formulae (7) $-$ (11) on the assumption that variable Y satisfies the inequality $y \leqslant Y < y + \Delta_y$.

On page 16 we have given the definition of an independent

discrete random variable. We shall now give the definition of an independent continuous random variable.

Definition 3. Two continuous random variables X and Y are independent if

$$P(x_1 \leqslant X < x_2,\ y_1 \leqslant Y < y_2)$$
$$= P(x_1 \leqslant X < x_2).P(y_1 \leqslant Y < y_2), \qquad (12)$$

where x_1, x_2 and y_1, y_2 are any real numbers. It is easy to prove that for two random variables to be independent it is *necessary and sufficient* that their joint two-dimensional distribution function equal the product of the marginal distribution functions of variable X and variable Y:

$$F(x, y) = F_1(x) \cdot F_2(y). \qquad (13)$$

The same theorem was given above for discrete variables.

1.2.4. *Moments of a two-dimensional variable*

Definition 1. The relative moment of a two-dimensional random variable (X,Y) is the expected value of

$$[(X - C)^l (Y - D)^k],$$

where l and k is the order of the moment and l, k are non-negative integers. C and D, which can be considered as the coordinates of an arbitrary point, are any real numbers.

Definition 2. If $C = D = 0$ the expected value of the product $x^l y^k$ is called the ordinary moment (or simply — the moment) of the two-dimensional random variable X, Y. These moments are usually denoted by the symbol m_{lk}.

In accordance with this definition

$$m_{lk} = E(X^l Y^k) = \lim_{\substack{a \to -\infty \\ b \to +\infty}} \lim_{\substack{c \to -\infty \\ d \to +\infty}} \sum_{a < x_i < b} \sum_{c < y_j < d} x_i^l y_j^k p_{ij}$$

$$= \sum_i \sum_j x_i^l y_j^k p_{ij}, \qquad (1)$$

where variable (X,Y) is discrete, and

$$m_{lk} = E(X^l Y^k)$$

$$= \lim_{\substack{a \to -\infty \\ b \to +\infty}} \lim_{\substack{c \to -\infty \\ d \to +\infty}} \int\limits_a^b \int\limits_c^d x^l y^k f(x,y)dx\,dy$$

$$= \int\limits_{-\infty}^\infty \int\limits_{-\infty}^\infty x^l y^k f(y,x)dx\,dy, \tag{2}$$

where variable (X,Y) is continuous.

The most frequent use is made of moments of the first and second order. Moments of the first order are the expected values of the random variables X and Y:

$$m_{10} = E(X^1 Y^0) = E(X) \tag{3}$$

and

$$m_{01} = E(X^0 Y^1) = E(Y). \tag{4}$$

The moment of the second order defined by formula

$$m_{11} = E(XY) \tag{5}$$

is called a product moment.

The remaining two moments of the second order are expressed by the formulae

$$m_{20} = E(X^2 Y^0) = E(X^2) \tag{6}$$

and

$$m_{02} = E(X^0 Y^2) = E(Y^2). \tag{7}$$

Definition 3. Moments with reference points $C = E(X)$ and $D = E(Y)$ are called central moments. They are usually denoted by μ_{lk}.

We then have

$$\mu_{lk} = E[(X - m_{10})^l (Y - m_{01})^k]. \tag{8}$$

Of course

$$\mu_{10} = E[(X - m_{10})^1 (Y - m_{01})^0] = 0 \tag{9}$$

and

$$\mu_{01} = E[(X - m_{10})^0 (Y - m_{01})^1] = 0. \tag{10}$$

In our further considerations three central moments of the second order will be of great importance:

$$\mu_{20} = E[(X - m_{10})^2] = V(X) \tag{11}$$

and

$$\mu_{02} = E[(Y - m_{01})^2] = V(Y). \tag{12}$$

These are variances of random variable X and random variable Y. The mixed central moment of the second order

$$\mu_{11} = E[(X - m_{10})(Y - m_{01})] \tag{13}$$

is known as a *covariance*. It is often denoted by $C(X,Y)$.

Central moments of a two-dimensional random variable can be expressed by ordinary moments, and vice versa. It is easy to show, for instance, that

$$\mu_{11} = m_{11} - m_{10} m_{01}. \tag{14}$$

Indeed

$$\mu_{11} = E[(X - m_{10})(Y - m_{01})] = E(XY) - m_{10} E(Y) -$$
$$- m_{01} E(X) + m_{10} m_{01} = m_{11} - m_{10} m_{01} - m_{01} m_{10} +$$
$$+ m_{10} m_{01} = m_{11} - m_{10} m_{01}.$$

Similarly, it can be proved that

$$\mu_{20} = m_{20} - m_{10}{}^2 \tag{15}$$

and

$$\mu_{02} = m_{02} - m_{01}{}^2. \tag{16}$$

The following important theorem can be proved for covariance.

THEOREM 1. If random variables X and Y are independent then the covariance $C(X,Y)$ of these variables equals zero.

Proof[1]. When variables X and Y are independent, then

$$p_{ij} = p_{i.} \cdot p_{.j}$$

(see 1.2.2., formula (15)).

---

[1] The proof is for discrete variables. The situation is similar when the variables are continuous.

Therefore

$$C(X, Y) = E(X - m_{10})(Y - m_{01})$$
$$= \sum_i (x_i - m_{10}) p_{i.} \sum_j (y_j - m_{01}) p_{.j} = \mu_{10} \cdot \mu_{01}.$$

On the basis of (9) and (10) we obtain

$$C(X, Y) = 0.$$

The converse theorem is not true.

In addition to the moments thus far defined there is another group of moments. They are called *conditional moments*. This term is used for moments of one of the variables X, Y, assuming that the remaining variable has a certain definite value.

In our further considerations we shall use two conditional moments: *the expected conditional value and the conditional variance*. If variable (X, Y) is continuous these parameters are expressed by the respective formulae

$$E(Y|X = x) = m_{01}(x) = \frac{\int\limits_{-\infty}^{\infty} y f(x, y) dy}{\int\limits_{-\infty}^{\infty} f(x, y) dy} = \int\limits_{-\infty}^{\infty} y f(y \mid x) dy, \quad (17)$$

$$V(Y \mid X = x) = \frac{\int\limits_{-\infty}^{\infty} [y - m_{01}(x)]^2 f(x, y) dy}{\int\limits_{-\infty}^{\infty} f(x, y) dy}$$

$$= \int\limits_{-\infty}^{\infty} [y - m_{01}(x)]^2 f(y \mid x) dy. \quad (18)$$

These are the conditional moments of variable Y. An analogous pair of formulae can be given for variable X.

When variables X and Y are independent, then

Library
I.U.P.
Indiana, Pa.

330.18 H369
c. 1

$$m_{01}(x) = \frac{\int\limits_{-\infty}^{\infty} y f_1(x) f_2(y) dy}{\int\limits_{-\infty}^{\infty} f_1(x) f_2(y) dy} = \int\limits_{-\infty}^{\infty} y f_2(y) dy = m_{01}.$$

1.2.5. Regression I

In a two-dimensional distribution of variable (X,Y) the expected conditional value $E(Y|X=x)$ is a function of the variable x. We may thus write:

$$E(Y \mid X = x) = g_1(x). \tag{1}$$

Substituting the simple symbol $\hat{y}$ for the expression $E(Y|X=x)$ in the above formula, we get

$$\hat{y} = g_1(x). \tag{2}$$

Equation (2) is known in mathematical statistics as the *equation of regression I of Y on X*.

By interchanging letters x and y in formulae (1) and (2) we get the regression equation of *variable X on Y*

$$\hat{x} = g_2(y). \tag{3}$$

If variable (X, Y) is continuous, then the geometrical representations of functions (2) and (3) will be lines. These lines are called *regression I lines*.

GRAPH 1.

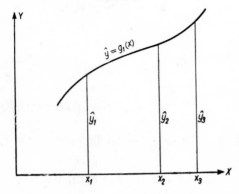

In Graph 1, the regression line of Y on X is shown. The ordinates of this curve represent the expected values of variable Y when variable $X = x$. If the equation of this line is known then to each value of variable X we can assign an expected value of variable Y.

GRAPH 2.

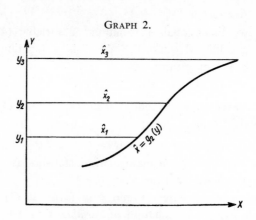

We shall prove the following

THEOREM 1. The expected value of the sum of the squared deviations of Y from the regression line is a minimum.

Proof. We are to prove that

$$E[Y - g(x)]^2 = \min.$$

But

$$E[Y - g(x)]^2 = \int_{-\infty}^{\infty} \int_{-\infty}^{\infty} [y - g(x)]^2 f(x, y) dx \, dy$$

$$= \int_{-\infty}^{\infty} f_1(x) dx \int_{-\infty}^{\infty} [y - g(x)]^2 f(y \mid x) dy.$$

As we know, $E(Y - u)^2 = $ minimum when $u = E(Y)$. Then

$$E(Y - u)^2 = V(Y).$$

Hence, for $E[Y-g(X)]^2$ to have a minimum it is necessary that

$$g(x) = E(Y \mid X = x),$$

because then

$$\int_{-\infty}^{\infty} [y - E(Y \mid X = x)]^2 f(y \mid x) dy$$

equals $V(Y|X = x)$, i.e. is a minimum. Therefore

$$E[Y - g(X)]^2 = \int_{-\infty}^{\infty} f_1(x) dx \int_{-\infty}^{\infty} [y - m_{01}(x)]^2 f(y \mid x) dy$$

$$= V(Y \mid X = x) = \min.$$

1.2.6. Regression II

In practice the shape of function $g(x)$ is rarely known. The usual procedure is to take a sample from a two-dimensional population and to draw a scatter diagram. The points on the graph follow a more or less distinct trend. This trend provides certain *information*; on its basis *the hypothesis may be formulated that function g(x) belongs to a certain class of functions* (e.g. to the class of linear, exponential or power functions or to the class of polynomials).

Graph 3 presents a scatter diagram drawn on the basis of statistical material collected in connection with studies on the relationship between hop consumption and the production of wort. The statistics were obtained from the Piast Brewery in Wrocław.

The trend of the points on the graph is so distinct that we can safely postulate the hypothesis that $g(x)$ belongs to the class of linear functions.

In order to determine the parameters of function $g(x)$ the expression $E[Y-g(x)]^2$ has to be made a minimum.

If $g(x) \equiv ax$ then to find the value of parameter a we have to minimize the value of the expression $S \equiv E[Y-ax]^2$.

We must calculate the derivative $\dfrac{\partial S}{\partial a}$ and equate it to zero. From the equation thus obtained a can be determined. The line determined in this way is called a *regression II line*. If the hypothesis concerning the class of functions to which

GRAPH 3.

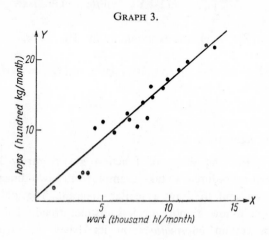

$g(x)$ belongs is true then the regression II line coincides with the regression I line. In applications we are always interested in regression I lines. Since the equations of these lines are usually not known we substitute regression II lines for regression I lines because the former are easier to determine. While doing this we are seldom free from worry as to whether the regression line has been properly determined because information provided by a scatter diagram is scanty and so the hypothesis regarding the class of functions to which $g(x)$ belongs may easily turn out to be wrong.

It happens sometimes that apart from a scatter diagram we may have at our disposal some additional information providing a basis for the hypothesis concerning the class of functions to which $g(x)$ belongs. For instance, sometimes we know the equation of asymptotes of the regression line, or we know that this line passes through the origin, or that it does not intersect the positive part of the *x*-axis and the negative part of the *y*-axis. Such information is very valuable. It always comes from sources *outside statistics*. One of the conditions of the effectiveness of statistical analysis is a *thorough knowledge of the subject being studied and of the division of science which is concerned with it*. This means, for instance, that to analyse by statistical methods the effectiveness of penicillin in fighting tuberculosis we need phthisiologists, and to study the effect of the price of butter on the consumption of edible oils we need economists. The knowledge of statistics alone is not sufficient. *Only the combination of statistical and non-statistical information can make our analysis fruitful.*

This principle is fully applicable to the determination of regression lines.

1.2.7. Linear regression

Definition 1. If an equation of regression is expressed by the formula

$$\hat{y} = a_{21} x + \beta_{20}, \tag{1}$$

we say that the regression of Y on X is linear.

Formula (1) is a regression equation of Y on X.

Quantities a_{21} and β_{20} are certain constants called *regression parameters*. The indices next to the parameters serve to distinguish the regression parameters of Y on X from those of X on Y. The first index is for the dependent variable in the regression equation and the second for the independent.

The linear regression equation of X on Y is expressed by the formula

$$\hat{x} = a_{12} y + \beta_{10}. \tag{2}$$

Linear regression

Sometimes we shall write equation (1) omitting indices, i.e.

$$\hat{y} = \alpha x + \beta. \tag{3}$$

In such cases it should be understood that our considerations refer to both types of regression lines, i.e. the regression of Y on X and the regression of X on Y.

*

If we know that in the distribution of the two-dimensional random variable (X,Y) the regression lines are straight, then in order to determine the value of parameters α and β we have to find the minimum for the expression

$$E[Y - \alpha X - \beta]^2 = \int_{R_2} [y - \alpha x - \beta]^2 dP,$$

where R_2 denotes the two-dimensional integration space and dP the differential of the two-dimensional distribution.

We calculate the partial derivatives of the expression in brackets on the left side, with respect to α and β.
We have

$$\frac{\partial}{\partial \alpha} E(Y - \alpha X - \beta)^2 = -2E[(Y - \alpha X - \beta)X]$$

and

$$\frac{\partial}{\partial \beta} E(Y - \alpha X - \beta)^2 = -2E(Y - \alpha X - \beta).$$

By equating both these derivatives to zero we obtain *a set of normal equations*

$$\begin{cases} E(XY - \alpha X^2 - \beta X) = 0, \\ E(Y - \alpha X - \beta) = 0. \end{cases} \tag{4}$$

After replacing the expected values by appropriate moments this set of equations can be written in the following form:

**

$$\begin{cases} m_{11} - \alpha m_{20} - \beta m_{10} = 0, \\ m_{01} - \alpha m_{10} - \beta = 0. \end{cases} \tag{5}$$

From the solution of the set of equations (5) we get:

$$\beta = \beta_{20} = m_{01} - a_{21}m_{10}, \tag{6}$$

$$a = a_{21} = \frac{m_{11} - m_{01} \cdot m_{10}}{m_{20} - m^2_{10}} . \tag{7}$$

On the basis of 1.2.4. (14), (15) and (16), formula (7) may be written thus:

$$a = a_{21} = \frac{\mu_{11}}{\mu_{20}} . \tag{8}$$

Similarly we get

$$\beta_{10} = m_{10} - a_{12}m_{01} \tag{9}$$

and

$$a_{12} = \frac{\mu_{11}}{\mu_{02}} . \tag{10}$$

Parameters a_{21}, and a_{12} are called *regression coefficients*. Substituting (6) in (1) and (9) in (2) we obtain the regression equations in the following form:

$$\hat{y} = a_{21}(x - m_{10}) + m_{01}, \tag{11}$$

$$\hat{x} = a_{12}(y - m_{01}) + m_{10}. \tag{12}$$

It follows from the above equations that both regression lines pass through the point with coordinates (m_{10}, m_{01}). We shall call this point *the population centre of gravity*.

The knowledge of regression equations allows us to express the stochastic dependence between random variables by a mathematical function describing numerically the relationship existing between these variables. The derivation of a function formula is very convenient since it allows us to assign to each value of a random variable, appearing as an argument, an appropriate value of the other variable appearing as a function.

We have stated on page 5 that the significance of regression line equations consists in the fact that they enable us to estimate particular values of one variable on the basis of the values assumed by the other variable. This estimate may be better or worse, more accurate, or less accurate. When we use the word "estimate" we must also introduce the notion of the "accuracy of the estimate" and create a measure of this accuracy.

Of course, *the smaller the sum of errors[1] that we commit by replacing the real values of the random variable by the values obtained from the regression line equation, the better the estimate will be.*

This statement lends itself to geometrical interpretation. The more closely the points are grouped around the regression line on the scatter diagram, or, what amounts to the same thing, the smaller is the dispersion of the points around the line, the better the estimate will be.

Let us call the quantity defined by formula

$$e_{y_i} = y_i - \hat{y}_i,$$

which is a realization of the random variable $\varepsilon_y = Y - \hat{y}$, the ith residual of the regression of Y on X, or in brief a *residual*.

As a measure of dispersion of points around the regression line the *residual variance* $V(\varepsilon_y)$ is generally used. It is determined by the formula

$$V(\varepsilon_y) = E(\varepsilon_y^2) = E(Y - \hat{y})^2. \tag{13}$$

If the regression line is a straight line, than

$$V(\varepsilon_y) = E[Y - (a_{21}X + \beta_{20})]^2 = E[Y - m_{01} + a_{21}m_{10} + \beta_{20} -$$
$$- a_{21}X - \beta_{20}]^2 = E[(Y - m_{01}) - a_{21}(X - m_{10})]^2$$
$$= E(W - a_{21}U)^2,$$

---

[1] We are not interested here in how these errors are measured: by absolute values, squared value, or in some other way.

where $W = Y - m_{01}$ and $U = X - m_{10}$.
And further

$$V(\varepsilon_y) = E(W^2 - 2a_{21}WU + a_{21}^2 U^2) = E(W^2) - 2a_{21}E(UW) + \\ + a_{21}^2 E(U^2) = \mu_{02} - 2a_{21}\mu_{11} + a_{21}^2\mu_{20}.$$

On the basis of (8) we have

$$V(\varepsilon_y) = \mu_{02} - 2a_{21}\mu_{11} + a_{21}\frac{\mu_{11}}{\mu_{20}} \cdot \mu_{20} = \mu_{02} - a_{21}\mu_{11}. \quad (14)$$

Analogously it can be shown that

$$V(\varepsilon_x) = \mu_{20} - a_{12}\mu_{11}. \quad (15)$$

The square root of the residual variance we shall call the *standard error of the estimate* and we shall denote it by the symbols σ_{21} and σ_{12} respectively for the regression of Y on X and the regression of X on Y. In this case

$$\sigma_{21} = \sqrt{\mu_{02} - a_{21}\mu_{11}} \quad (16)$$

and

$$\sigma_{12} = \sqrt{\mu_{20} - a_{12}\mu_{11}}. \quad (17)$$

Using the symbols for variance and covariance we may present formula (14) in the following way:

$$V(\varepsilon_y) = V(Y) - a_{21}C(XY) = V(Y) - a_{21}^2 V(X). \quad (18)$$

Hence, it follows that

$$V(\varepsilon_y) \leqslant V(Y)$$

or, what amounts to the same thing, that

$$\frac{V(\varepsilon_y)}{V(Y)} \leqslant 1, \quad V(Y) \neq 0. \quad (19)$$

In the conclusion of our comments on the two-dimensional regression line let us quote two important theorems and their proofs.

* THEOREM 1. If a regression I line is a straight line then the regression II line coincides with the regression I line.

Proof. By assumption we have

$$E(Y|X = x) = ax + \beta.$$

Taking the mathematical expectation of both sides of the equation we obtain:

$$E[E(Y|X = x)] = aE(X) + \beta.$$

But

$$E[E(Y|X = x)] = E(Y) = m_{01}.$$

Hence

$$m_{01} = am_{10} + \beta.$$

This means that the regression I line passes through the centre of gravity. We have shown on page 31 that the regression II line also passes through this point. This enables us to introduce new variables:

$$U = X - m_{10}, \qquad W = Y - m_{01}.$$

Consequently the equation for regression I will assume the following form:

$$E(W|U = u) = au,$$

and the equation for regression II will be expressed by the formula

$$\hat{w} = a'u,$$

where a' denotes the regression coefficient in this equation. Therefore

$$E(W - a'U)^2 = E[(W - aU) + (aU - a'U)]^2$$
$$= E(W - aU)^2 + 2E(W - aU)[(a - a')U] + E(aU - a'U)^2.$$

The expression

$$E(W - aU)[(a - a')U]$$

is zero for each determined value of U since it follows from the assumption of linearity that

$$E(W) = aE(U).$$

Thus we have

$$E(W - a'U)^2 = E(W - aU)^2 + E(aU - a'U)^2.$$

Since the first term on the right side of the equation does not depend on a', then the expression $E(W-a'U)^2$ has a minimum for the same value of a' as the expression $E(aU-a'U)^2$, and that expression has a minimum when

$$E(aU - a'U)^2 = 0, \text{ i.e. when } a = a'.$$

But a' is determined by the condition

$$E(Y - a'X - \beta)^2 = \text{minimum},$$

which is equivalent to the condition

$$E(W - a'U)^2 = \text{minimum},$$

and this condition is fulfilled when $a = a'$. Therefore, when the regression I line is straight it coincides with the regression II line.

THEOREM 2. When the regression I line is a straight line then the residual variance is a minimum.

Proof. The parameters of the regression II line are determined by the condition (see p. 30):

$$E(\varepsilon_y^2) = E(Y - a'X - \beta')^2 = \text{minimum}.$$

It follows from Theorem 1 that both the regression I and regression II lines coincide in the case of linear regression. This means that for the regression I line this condition is also fulfilled, which proves that the theorem is correct. The theorem proved is a special case of theorem 1 on page 26.

1.2.8. Correlation. Correlation ratio and correlation coefficient

On page 32 in formula (13) the definition was given for the residual variance as a measure of the dispersion of points (x,y) around the regression line.

However, the application of the residual variance is not limited to measuring only the dispersion of points around the regression line. Let us note that the smaller the dispersion the *closer* is the bond between random variables X and Y. When all the points lie on the regression line there is no dispersion at all and $V(\varepsilon) = 0$. This is a case of a functional relationship between variables X and Y and not of a stochastic relationship.

It follows that quantity $V(\varepsilon)$ may be used for measuring the dependence between two random variables. Indeed the residual variance is used for this purpose although not in the form described in the definition.

A measure of dependence between two random variables should meet the following requirements:

1) it should have no dimension;
2) it should be normalized and assume values belonging to a certain finite numerical interval;
3) it should assume increasing values when the dependence becomes stronger, and decreasing values when it becomes weaker;
4) it should not depend on whether the dependence of X on Y is measured, or vice versa.

None of these requirements is satisfied by $V(\varepsilon)$. With the help of several simple mathematical operations, however, we can construct a quantity which will fully satisfy these requirements. In order to satisfy requirements 1) and 2) it is sufficient to divide $V(\varepsilon_y)$ by $V(Y)$ or $V(\varepsilon_x)$ by $V(X)$. Indeed, since $V(\varepsilon_y)$ and $V(Y)$ are of the same dimension, then

$$\frac{V(\varepsilon_y)}{V(Y)}$$

has no dimension.

It follows from formula (19) on p. 33 that

$$0 \leqslant \frac{V(\varepsilon_y)}{V(Y)} \leqslant 1,$$

which means that this quantity is normalized in the interval [0,1].

Requirement 3) will be met if instead of $\dfrac{V(\varepsilon_y)}{V(Y)}$ and $\dfrac{V(\varepsilon_x)}{V(X)}$ we introduce the quantities

$$\eta_y^2 = 1 - \frac{V(\varepsilon_y)}{V(Y)}, \tag{1}$$

$$\eta_x^2 = 1 - \frac{V(\varepsilon_x)}{V(X)}. \tag{2}$$

Quantities η_y and η_x defined by formulae (1) and (2) are known as *correlation ratios*[1].
Of course

$$0 \leqslant \eta_y \leqslant 1. \tag{3}$$

The correlation ratio η_y equals one if and only if $V(\varepsilon_y) = 0$, i.e. when the dependence between random variables X and Y is of a functional type.
When

$$\eta_y \neq 0$$

it is said that the random variables *are correlated with one another*. When

$$\eta_y = 0$$

we say that they are uncorrelated. All that has been said about correlation ratio η_y also applies to η_x.

The lack of a correlation between random variables does not mean, by any means, that these variables are stochastically independent. As we know (see p. 21, formula (13)) random variables X and Y are independent if

$$F(x.y) = F_1(x).F_2(y), \tag{4}$$

and they are uncorrelated if

$$\eta_y = 0 \text{ or } \eta_x = 0. \tag{5}$$

Relations (4) and (5) are not equivalent.

---

[1] This measure was introduced by K. Pearson.

In order to satisfy requirement 4) we assume that both regression I lines are straight lines. Therefore

$$V(\varepsilon_y) = V(Y) - a_{21}.C(XY)$$

(see p. 33, formula (18)), and analogously

$$V(\varepsilon_x) = V(X) - a_{12}.C(XY).$$

Hence

$$\eta_y^2 = 1 - \frac{V(Y) - a_{21}C(XY)}{V(Y)} = a_{21}\frac{C(XY)}{V(Y)} = a_{21}\frac{\mu_{11}}{\mu_{02}} = a_{21}.a_{12}$$

(see (12), (13) on p. 23).
Similarly

$$\eta_x^2 = 1 - \frac{V(X) - a_{12}C(XY)}{V(X)} = a_{12}\frac{C(XY)}{V(X)} = a_{12}\frac{\mu_{11}}{\mu_{20}} = a_{12}.a_{21}.$$

Therefore, when the regression lines are straight lines

$$\eta_y = \eta_x.$$

The quantity

$$\varrho = \sqrt{a_{12}.a_{21}} \tag{6}$$

is called the *correlation coefficient*. Since the correlation coefficient is a special case of the correlation ratio, then on the basis of (1) we also have

$$\varrho^2 \leqslant 1 \quad \text{or} \quad -1 \leqslant \varrho \leqslant 1.$$

When $\varrho > 0$ we say that between random variables X and Y there is *positive correlation*. In cases of positive correlation an increase in the value of one variable is accompanied by an increase in the expected value of the other. Let us note that

$$\varrho = \sqrt{a_{12} \cdot a_{21}} = \frac{\mu_{11}}{\sqrt{\mu_{20} \cdot \mu_{02}}}.$$

By this convention the sign of the correlation coefficient depends on the sign of μ_{11}.

On the other hand,

$$\alpha_{12} = \frac{\mu_{11}}{\mu_{20}}, \qquad \alpha_{21} = \frac{\mu_{11}}{\mu_{02}} .$$

Since $\mu_{20} > 0$ and $\mu_{02} > 0$, the signs of α_{12} and α_{21} also depend on the sign of μ_{11}. Hence, when $\varrho > 0$, $\alpha_{12} > 0$ and $\alpha_{21} > 0$. But α_{12} and α_{21} are slopes of the regression lines. Therefore, when $\varrho > 0$ the regression line $\hat{y} = \alpha_{21}x + \beta_{20}$ forms a sharp angle with the x-axis which means that $\hat{y}$ is an increasing function of x.

When $\varrho < 0$ we deal with negative correlation and then an increase in the value of one variable is accompanied by a decrease in the conditional expected value of the other.

The position of the regression lines for a positive correlation is shown on Graph 1 and the position of these lines for a negative correlation is shown on Graph 2.

GRAPH 1.   GRAPH 2.

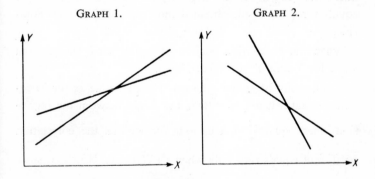

The correlation coefficient equals $+1$ or -1 only when all points (x,y) lie on the straight line.

Let us now prove

THEOREM 1. When $\varrho^2 = 1$ the two regression lines coincide.

* *Proof.* Let us assume that $\varrho = +1$ (the proof is analogous when we assume that $\varrho = -1$). In this case it follows from the definition of the correlation coefficient that

$$\varrho^2 = a_{12} \cdot a_{21} = 1.$$

The parameter a_{12} is the tangent of the angle that the regression line $\hat{x} = a_{12}y + \beta_{10}$ forms with the y-axis. The slope of this line, with reference to the horizontal axis, equals $\dfrac{1}{a_{12}}$. The inclination parameter of the regression line $\hat{y} = a_{20} + \beta_{01}$ with reference to the horizontal axis equals a_{21}. The tangent of the angle contained between two regression lines then is

$$\frac{\dfrac{1}{a_{12}} - a_{21}}{1 + \dfrac{a_{21}}{a_{12}}} = \frac{1 - a_{12} \cdot a_{21}}{a_{12} + a_{21}} = 0.$$

Since the tangent of an angle equals zero when the angle equals zero, the result obtained indicates that the lines coincide.

When the correlation coefficient equals zero, the random variables X and Y are uncorrelated.

It can easily be shown (the proof is the same as for Theorem 1) that when $\varrho = 0$ then the angle between the regression lines equals $\dfrac{\pi}{2}$. Let us note further that the correlation coefficient equals zero only when $C(XV) = 0$. However, since

$$a_{12} = \frac{C(XY)}{V(X)} \qquad a_{21} = \frac{C(XY)}{V(Y)}$$

then if $\varrho^2 = 0$, $a_{12} = 0$ and $a_{21} = 0$. Thus, when variables X and Y are not correlated the regression lines intersect at the angle $\frac{1}{2}\pi$ and the regression line of Y on X is parallel to the horizontal axis and the regression line of X on Y is parallel to the vertical axis (Graph 3).

On page 23 we proved the theorem that if random variables X and Y are independent, the covariance $C(XY)$ equals zero. We shall now express this theorem in a slightly different form.

THEOREM 2. If variables X and Y are independent, then they are also uncorrelated.

The converse theorem is not true. The theorem contrapositive to Theorem 2 is of great practical and theoretical importance. It is:

THEOREM 3. If random variables X and Y are correlated they are also dependent.

GRAPH 3.

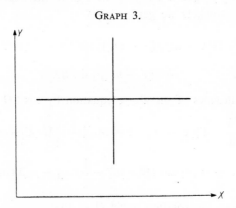

Theorem 3 does not have to be proved since it is a theorem contrapositive to Theorem 2, which is true. As we know, two contrapositive theorems must be either both false, or both true.

To conclude our discussion of the correlation coefficient we shall prove the important

THEOREM 4. For any random variables X and Y there is always a linear transformation which can bring these variables to the form in which the correlation coefficient ϱ between the transformed variables equals zero.

Proof. Using known formulae for translating and rotating the coordinate system we have

$$X' = (X - m_{10}) \cos \Theta + (Y - m_{01}) \sin \Theta,$$

$$Y' = - (X - m_{10}) \sin \Theta + (Y - m_{01}) \cos \Theta.$$

For variables X' and Y' to be uncorrelated it is necessary and sufficient that $C(X'Y') = E(X'Y') = 0$.
In accordance with formula (13) item 1.2.4.:

$$E(X'Y') = E\{[(X - m_{10}) \cos \Theta + (Y - m_{01}) \sin \Theta] [- (X -$$
$$- m_{10}) \sin \Theta + (Y - m_{01}) \cos \Theta]\}.$$

After multiplying and bringing the sign of the expected value within the brackets we get

$$E(X'Y') = E[(X - m_{10}) (Y - m_{01})] \cos 2\Theta - \frac{1}{2} [E(X - m_{10})^2 -$$
$$- E(Y - m_{01})^2] \sin 2\Theta.$$

Divide both sides of the above equation by $\cos 2\Theta$

$$\frac{E(X'Y')}{\cos 2\Theta} = E[(X - m_{10}) (Y - m_{01})] - \frac{1}{2} [E(X - m_{10})^2 -$$

$$- E(Y - m_{01})^2] \tan 2\Theta = \mu_{11} - \frac{1}{2} (\mu_{20} - \mu_{02}) \tan 2\Theta.$$

If we choose the rotation angle Θ so that

$$\tan 2\Theta = \frac{2\mu_{11}}{\mu_{20} - \mu_{02}}, \quad \text{we get} \tag{7}$$

$$E(X'Y') = 0, \quad \text{and hence} \quad \varrho(X'Y') = 0.$$

Let us note in passing that if we determine angle Θ from formula (7) and if

$$\lambda = \tan \Theta,$$

then the line having the equation

$$(y - m_{01}) = \lambda(x - m_{10}) \qquad (8)$$

has the property that the sum of the squares of the distances of points (x,y) from this line is a minimum. The straight line (8) is known as the *orthogonal regression* line. It follows from formula (8) that this line passes through the centre of gravity. After some elementary transformations we obtain a formula for the slope of line (8)

$$\lambda = \frac{1}{2\mu_{11}} \left[\mu_{20} - \mu_{02} \pm \sqrt{(\mu_{20} - \mu_{02})^2 + 4\mu_{11}^2} \right]. \qquad (9)$$

1.2.9. The two-dimensional normal distribution

The distribution of the two-dimensional random variable (X,Y) with a density determined by the formula

$$\varphi(x,y) \qquad (1)$$

$$= \frac{1}{2\pi\, \sigma_1\, \sigma_2 \sqrt{1 - \varrho^2}}\, e^{- \frac{1}{2(1-\varrho^2)} \left[\frac{(x-m_1)^2}{\sigma_1^2} - 2\varrho\, \frac{(x-m_1)}{\sigma_1} \cdot \frac{(y-m_2)}{\sigma_2} + \frac{(y-m_2)^2}{\sigma_2^2} \right]}$$

where

$$\sigma_1 = \sqrt{V(X)}, \quad \sigma_2 = \sqrt{V(Y)}, \quad m_1 = E(X), \quad m_2 = E(Y),$$

is called a *two-dimensional normal distribution*.

The great practical importance of distribution (1) follows from the generalized Central Limit Theorem on two-dimensional variables. On Graph 1 the density surface for a two-dimensional normal distribution is presented.

THEOREM 1. If the density of random variable (X,Y) is expressed by formula (1) and if the correlation coefficient ϱ between variables X and Y equals zero, then variables X and Y are independent.

GRAPH 1.

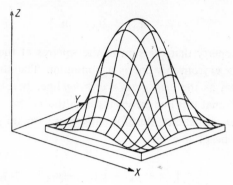

Proof. If $\varrho = 0$ then

$$\varphi(x, y) = \frac{1}{2\pi\,\sigma_1\,\sigma_2}\, e^{-\frac{1}{2}\left[\frac{(x-m_1)^2}{\sigma_1^2} + \frac{(y-m_2)^2}{\sigma_2^2}\right]}$$

$$= \frac{1}{\sqrt{2\pi}\,\sigma_1}\, e^{-\frac{1}{2}\left(\frac{x-m_1}{\sigma_1}\right)^2} \cdot \frac{1}{\sqrt{2\pi}\,\sigma_2}\, e^{-\frac{1}{2}\left(\frac{x-m_2}{\sigma_2}\right)^2}.$$

Denoting

$$\varphi_1(x) = \frac{1}{\sqrt{2\pi}\,\sigma_1}\, e^{-\frac{1}{2}\left(\frac{x-m_1}{\sigma_1}\right)^2}, \tag{2}$$

$$\varphi_2(y) = \frac{1}{\sqrt{2\pi}\,\sigma_2}\, e^{-\frac{1}{2}\left(\frac{y-m_2}{\sigma_2}\right)^2} \tag{3}$$

we have

$$\varphi(x, y) = \varphi_1(x) \cdot \varphi_2(y).$$

After integrating both sides of the above identity with respect to each variable, we get

$$\int\limits_{-\infty}^{x} \int\limits_{-\infty}^{y} \varphi(x, y)dx\, dy = \int\limits_{-\infty}^{x} \varphi_1(x)dx \cdot \int\limits_{-\infty}^{y} \varphi_2(y)dy.$$

Using the definition of the two-dimensional random variable distribution function we may write

$$F(x, y) = F_1(x) \cdot F_2(y).$$

We have obtained the necessary and sufficient condition for the independence of the random variables (item 1.2.3., formula (13)). Thus the theorem has been proved.

THEOREM 2. The conditional density $\varphi(y|x)$ in a two-dimensional normal distribution is the density of a normal distribution with the following parameters:

$$E(Y \mid X = x) = m_2 + a_{21}(x - m_1), \qquad (4)$$

$$V(Y \mid X = x) = (1 - \varrho^2)V(Y). \qquad (5)$$

Proof. On the basis of formula (11), item 1.2.3.

$$\varphi(y \mid x) = \frac{\varphi(x, y)}{\varphi_1(x)}.$$

For convenience let us denote

$$u = \frac{x - m_1}{\sigma_1}, \qquad v = \frac{y - m_2}{\sigma_2}.$$

Then

$$\varphi(y \mid x) = \frac{e^{-\frac{1}{2(1-\sigma^2)}[u^2 - 2\varrho uv + v^2]}}{2\pi\,\sigma_1\,\sigma_2\,\sqrt{1-\varrho^2}} : \frac{e^{-\frac{u^2}{2}}}{\sqrt{2\pi\,\sigma_1}}$$

$$= \frac{e^{-\frac{(v^2 - 2\varrho uv + \varrho^2 u^2)}{2(1-\varrho^2)}}}{\sqrt{2\pi\,\sigma_2}\,\sqrt{1-\varrho^2}} = \frac{e^{-\frac{1}{2}\left(\frac{v - \varrho u}{\sqrt{1-\varrho^2}}\right)^2}}{\sqrt{2\pi\,\sigma_2}\,\sqrt{1-\varrho^2}}$$

$$= \frac{e^{-\frac{1}{2}\left[\frac{y - m_2 - \varrho\frac{\sigma_2}{\sigma_1}(x-m_1)}{\sigma_2\sqrt{1-\varrho^2}}\right]^2}}{\sqrt{2\pi\,\sigma_2}\,\sqrt{1-\varrho^2}} = \frac{e^{-\frac{1}{2}\left[\frac{y - m_2 - a_{21}(x-m_1)}{\sigma_2\sqrt{1-\varrho^2}}\right]^2}}{\sqrt{2\pi\,\sigma_2}\,\sqrt{1-\varrho^2}}.$$

Formula (4) represents the regression equation of Y on X. Since a regression I line is a locus of conditional expected values then it follows from the theorem proved above that:

Corollary 1. Regression lines in a two-dimensional normal distribution are *straight lines*. On the right-hand side of the equation in formula (5) only constant quantities appear. Hence follows

Corollary 2. In a two-dimensional normal distribution, the conditional variance $V(Y|X = x)$ is a *constant quantity*. Both corollaries, as we shall see, are of great practical importance.

The density surface of a normal distribution shown on Graph 1 is a geometrical interpretation of equation (1). The intersection of this surface with the plane parallel to plane *XOY* is called *the equiprobability curve*. Such curves in a normal distribution are ellipses. The equation of the family of these ellipses is as follows:

$$\frac{(x - m_1)^2}{\sigma_1^2} - 2\varrho \frac{(x - m_1)}{\sigma_1} \cdot \frac{(y - m_2)}{\sigma_2} + \frac{(y - m_2)^2}{\sigma_2^2} = C^2, \quad (6)$$

where C is a variable parameter dependent upon the parameter of the intersecting plane. The centre of this family of ellipses is the centre of gravity, i.e. the point with coordinates $[m_1, m_2]$. The regression lines are the diameters of the ellipses conjugate to the diameters parallel to the coordinate axes.

GRAPH 2.

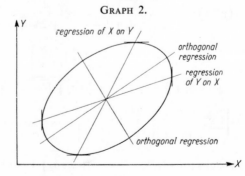

The major axis of the ellipse coincides with the orthogonal regression line (Graph 2).

When $\varrho = 0$, equation (6) assumes the form

$$\frac{(x-m_1)^2}{\sigma_1^2} + \frac{(y-m_2)^2}{\sigma_2^2} = C^2. \tag{7}$$

The major and minor axes of ellipse (7) are parallel to the corresponding coordinate axes, X and Y. When $\varrho = 0$ and $\sigma_1 = \sigma_2$, the ellipses become circles.

Since the sum of the random variables

$$\frac{(x-m_1)^2}{\sigma_1^2} + \frac{(y-m_2)^2}{\sigma_2^2} = u^2 + v^2$$

has the χ^2 distribution with two degrees of freedom, the probability that a random point (x,y) is located within the area determined by curve (7) is

$$P\{\chi^2 < C^2\}.$$

The probability that point (x, y) is located within the area determined by curve (6), is the same.

The area determined by the equiprobability ellipse may be considered as a characteristic of the dispersion in a two-dimensional normal distribution. The measure of this area is, then, a generalized measure of dispersion comprising two-dimensional random variables.

The values of the distribution function and of the density function of a two-dimensional normal distribution are given in tables (see [40] and [44]). These tables, however, are not in general use, and therefore are not easily accessible. For this reason, the following expansion of the density function of a normal distribution into a series (see [7], [52], [54]) has great practical importance. It can be proved that when $m_1 = m_2 = 0$, then

$$\varphi(x, y) = \frac{1}{2\pi\,\sigma_1\,\sigma_2\,\sqrt{1-\varrho^2}}\; e^{-\frac{1}{2\sqrt{1-\varrho^2}}\left[\frac{x^2}{\sigma_1^2} - \frac{2\varrho\,xy}{\sigma_1\,\sigma_2} + \frac{y^2}{\sigma_2^2}\right]}$$

$$= \frac{1}{\sigma_1\,\sigma_2}\sum_0^\infty \frac{\Phi^{(\nu+1)}\left(\dfrac{x}{\sigma_1}\right)\Phi^{(\nu+1)}\left(\dfrac{y}{\sigma_2}\right)}{\nu!}\,\varrho^\nu, \qquad (8)$$

where

$$\Phi(x) = \frac{1}{\sqrt{2\pi}}\int_{-\infty}^x e^{-\frac{u^2}{2}}\,du.$$

Hence, when $x = y = 0$,

$$\sum_0^\infty \frac{[\Phi^{(\nu+1)}(0)]^2}{\nu!}\,\varrho^\nu = \frac{1}{2\pi\,\sqrt{1-\varrho^2}}.$$

Integrating both sides with respect to ϱ, we get

$$\sum_1^\infty \frac{[\Phi^{(\nu)}(0)]^2}{\nu!}\,\varrho^\nu = \frac{1}{2\pi}\int_0^\varrho \frac{d\varrho}{\sqrt{1-\varrho^2}} = \frac{1}{2\pi}\arcsin\varrho.$$

On the other hand, after integrating formula (8) we get

$$\int_{-\infty}^x\int_{-\infty}^y \varphi(u,v)du\,dv = \sum_0^\infty \frac{\Phi^{(\nu)}\left(\dfrac{x}{\sigma_1}\right)\Phi^{(\nu)}\left(\dfrac{y}{\sigma_2}\right)}{\nu!}\,\varrho^\nu.$$

Of course, if $x = y = 0$, then

$$\int_{-\infty}^0\int_{-\infty}^0 \varphi(u,v)du\,dv = [\Phi(0)]^2 + \sum_1^\infty \frac{[\Phi^{(\nu)}(0)]^2}{\nu!}\,\varrho^\nu.$$

Since, however, $\Phi(0) = \tfrac{1}{2}$, we finally have

$$\int_{-\infty}^0\int_{-\infty}^0 \varphi(u,v)du\,dv = \frac{1}{4} + \arcsin\varrho \qquad (9)$$

** (see [7]).

1.3. Non-linear regression in R_2

In 1.2.5. we have defined the regression I line (formula (1), p. 25). To determine the regression equation of Y on X we used the notation

$$\hat{y} = g_1(x).$$

The concrete form of the regression curve equation is usually not known. In order to know the equation of the regression curve it is necessary to know the distribution of variable (X,Y), and this is seldom possible in practice.

If the distribution of variable (X,Y) is not known, various procedures may be used. We shall discuss the more important of them.

1. The hypothesis concerning the shape of curve $g_1(x)$ based on the hypothesis concerning the distribution of variable (X,Y)

If the collection of values that can be assumed by the random variable (X,Y) is so large that it cannot be analysed as a whole, then the only *statistical* source of information about the distribution of variable (X,Y) is a sample. All other information about the distribution of variables (X,Y) is *non-statistical information* (see p. 29). In analysing the distribution of a random variable we may, and should, take into consideration *all* the information in our possession, both statistical and non-statistical. Suppose that on the basis of available information we have postulated a statistical hypothesis H, according to which the distribution of random variable (X,Y) is normal. Let us also suppose that the testing[1] of this hypothesis has not provided a basis for rejecting it. In this case we may assume that function $g_1(x)$ is linear, because if the hypothesis is true, then, according to Corollary 1 (1.2.9.) the regression lines are straight lines.

---

[1] It will be discussed in Chapter 4.

2. The hypothesis concerning the shape of curve $g_1(x)$ based on non-statistical information

A hypothesis concerning the shape of the regression curve can often be based on information not directly related to the distribution of random variable (X,Y), but pertaining to the phenomenon that this variable describes mathematically. For instance, in smoothing out a broken curve of a time series representing the growth of population of a country within a certain period of time, there are reasons to assume that such a curve will be exponential if only we make a generally acceptable assumption that the rate of population increase during the period under consideration was not subject to serious fluctuations.

3. The hypothesis concerning the shape of curve $g_1(x)$ based on a scatter diagram

If non-statistical information is so scanty that we cannot postulate any hypothesis concerning the shape of the curve $g_1(x)$, then the only way out is to take a sample, to draw a scatter diagram and to analyse it. If the points on the diagram are so distributed that a distinct tendency in the form of a clearly marked trend is noticeable, then on the basis of the shape of this trend a certain class of functions can be chosen that should be suitable for approximating the distribution of points on the scatter diagram. The parameters of a function approximating the distribution and belonging to this class are determined by an appropriate method (e.g. the method of least squares).

What is striking in this type of approach is the high degree of arbitrariness. This approach cannot be taken when there are more than 3 dimensions, since in such cases it is not possible to draw a scatter diagram. For this reason non-linear regression is much less often used than linear regression.

It is worth stressing at this point, that non-linear regression can always be approximated by a broken curve and thus *non-linear regression can be reduced to linear regression*.

In many important applications, non-linear regression can be reduced to a linear form by an appropriate choice and introduction of new variables[1].

For these reasons in recent studies on probability and mathematical statistics non-linear regression is either completely omitted (e.g. [7], [21]) or discussed only briefly and in general terms (e.g. [28], [33]).

---

[1] This will be discussed in Chapter 5.

2. THE APPLICATION OF REGRESSION AND CORRELATION TO ECONOMIC RESEARCH

2.1. On the relation between economics and mathematics, on statistics and econometrics

The constant changes to which production processes are subject as a result of the rapid development of science and technique, pose more and more difficult problems to economic science. The historical and descriptive methods traditionally used by the social sciences are no longer adequate to solve these problems. The *ability to predict* is becoming an indispensable tool in the proper management of the production processes. The need for acquiring this ability is felt both in a capitalist economy which continually tries to free itself from the vicissitudes of market domination, and in a socialist economy where the growth targets are determined on the basis of long-run economic plans.

The ordinary meaning of the word "predict" is obvious. The term "scientific forecasting", however, requires some explanation. *By scientific forecasting we understand in this context every judgment, the accuracy of which is a random event with a probability known to the degree of exactness sufficient for practical purposes.* It follows from this definition that a scientific forecast is always a *statistical hypothesis*. Scientific forecasting is impossible without comparing different quantities, *without measuring*, without using numbers. For this reason contemporary economics makes use of mathematics[1] to a growing extent; especially useful are the

---

[1] An exhaustive survey of applications of mathematics to economics can be found in studies [2], [58].

theory of probability, mathematical statistics and econometrics.

The knowledge of causal relations existing between a given phenomenon and other phenomena is indispensable for scientific forecasting. If the relation between them is very strong it can be presented as a mathematical function. In the social sciences, as a rule, we do not deal with functional relationships. This is due to the complexity of the nature of the phenomena studied. The relationships between them are usually of a stochastic nature (see p. 2). A specialized branch of mathematical statistics dealing with stochastic relationships is the theory of regression and correlation (which we shall also call correlation analysis).

So far, correlation analysis has not been very extensively used by economists in their normal work. It is not difficult to explain why this is so. If a research method is to find a wide range of applications it is necessary for it to be: 1) sufficiently *universal*, i.e. suitable for solving a large number of different problems; 2) not too difficult, and easily popularized. We shall discuss the second of these conditions in Chapter 3. Here we shall try to show that the first condition is satisfied: that economics provides many interesting problems which can be solved only by correlation methods.

Since the times of A. Cournot, political economy has employed functions in its research with ever greater frequency and daring. Cournot himself, being a mathematician, believed that economics, like mechanics, can freely use the concept of a function without the necessity of concerning itself unduly with the exact form of the function. Every function can be accepted as given, on the assumption that such a function actually exists in real life and, one way or another, can always be determined when the need arises. This point of view has been accepted by other economists such as Gossen, Pareto, Marshall and Keynes, to name just a few. This standpoint is acceptable if it is remembered that the curves used in mathematical economics are, in fact, regression curves when looked upon from a statistical point of view because the variables employed in economics are not ordinary, but random variables. This is the reason for a great number of applications of correlation analysis to economics. We shall not confine ourselves to this general justification of the suitability of correlation methods for economic research, but shall also discuss the more important fields of their application.

Before we do so, however, let us say a few words about *econometrics*. Among the problems with which this science deals is the elaboration of numerical research methods for use in economics. The first place among them is occupied by statistical methods. Here is what Tintner has to say, in his book "Econometrics": "Econometricians also make use of statistical methods to test certain hypotheses about the unknown population. This procedure is useful in the testing and verification of economic laws" (see [57], p. 18). The above sentence does not define the subject of econometrics but pertinently indicates with what this science deals. And here is how the founders of the Econometric Society interpret its scientific tasks:

— Econometric Society is an international association whose objective is the development of economic theory in conjunction with statistics and mathematics (see [61], p. 5).

In the majority of works on econometrics we find examples of the application of statistical methods to economics. Correlation analysis, and particularly regression theory are the most useful. Mathematical economics treats the economic categories with which it deals, as *mathematical variables*, and analyses functional relationships between these variables. When a dependence between a pair of variables is considered, it may be presented as a curve. The curves with which mathematical economics deals may be divided into three groups.

To the first group belong the curves describing the relationship between a pair of *economic variables*, e.g. the relationship between demand and price, costs and production, consumption and income, etc.

The second group consists of the curves describing the relationship between an *economic variable and time*. They are called time curves. And finally, to the third group belong the curves describing the relationship between an *economic variable and a technological variable*. We deal with this type of relationship when we study the effect of the quality of raw materials on the cost of production or on the productivity of labour. The third group of curves we shall call techno-economic curves.

We shall discuss here the most important curves belonging to the first group: want curves, personal income distribution curves, demand curves and cost curves. Curves belonging to the second group will be considered together in the section entitled "Time Curves". Curves belonging to the third group will also be discussed together in the section called "Techno-Economic Curves".

2.2. More important applications of regression and correlation theory in economic research

2.2.1. Want curves

In order to live, man has to satisfy his various wants. Speaking most generally, these wants may be divided into physical and spiritual wants. To satisfy his wants man has to develop appropriate kinds of activities. One of the forms of such activity is labour. Labour creates use values, i.e. provides the objects of nature with the ability to satisfy human needs. In a society where the division of labour is well developed, people receive objects necessary to satisfy their needs on the market in exchange for money. The more money they have, the better they can satisfy their needs. The desire to satisfy one's needs manifests itself externally as the pursuit of money.

The feeling of displeasure that a man sometimes experiences when his needs are not satisfied is the driving power inducing him to develop an activity leading to the satisfaction of his needs. *The lack of such a feeling is tantamount to the lack of wants.*

Human wants are, as a rule, unlimited. However, the means, that people have at their disposal for the satisfaction of their needs are limited. *This results in a continuous conflict consisting in the necessity of making a decision as to which of the wants is to be satisfied.*

Let S be the sum of financial resources which person Z has at his disposal to meet his needs during period T. Let Q_1, Q_2... be various needs of this person, and S_1, S_2... the amounts required to meet needs Q_1, Q_2... Amounts S_1, S_2... we shall call the prices of needs Q_1, Q_2...

The following inequality is obviously satisfied:

$$S < \sum_i S_i$$

and person Z can satisfy only some of his needs. The choice must be made so that

$$S \geqslant \sum_{i=1}^{k} S_i,$$

where k denotes the number of needs satisfied.

In choosing those needs that are to be satisfied from the amount S, person Z, if he behaves rationally, must act so as to minimize the displeasure caused by the inability to satisfy all his needs.

Among the most important human wants are those which are necessary to his existence. These wants we shall call *basic wants.* If the sum S that person Z has at his disposal is small, then it will be spent entirely on his basic wants. Until they are satisfied person Z *has no freedom in choosing the wants to be satisfied.* Let us denote by S' the minimum amount of money necessary to keep Z alive during period T under conditions that are not detrimental to the existence and development of his body. In this case, assuming that Z behaves rationally, sum S will be spent entirely on the satisfaction of his basic needs unless S is greater than S'.

Suppose that at a certain moment t_0 person Z has at his disposal the sum $S = S'$, and that at moments $t_0 + rT$ ($r = 1,2,...$) he will receive amounts S_r, increasing with r. Then, at the moment $t_0 + rT$, person Z will have at his disposal the amount $S_r = S' + S_r''$. The sum S_r'' is the amount that Z has at moment t_r after meeting his basic needs during period T. The sum S'' we shall call the sum of *free decision.*

Let us consider what behaviour should be expected from people when the sums of free decision that are at their disposal increase. Two types of situations may develop here:

1) The whole sum S'' will be earmarked to *satisfy always the same, permanent group of needs.*

2) As S'' grows, *new needs* will be satisfied. The group of satisfied needs will *change and expand with the growth of S''.*

We know from experience that the first type of situation rarely occurs in practice. In conformity with the psychological law[1] the displeasure related to an unsatisfied need decreases as the need is satisfied. This means that *as personal incomes increase people spend money from the sums of free decision at their disposal to satisfy new and different needs and do not always spend these sums for the satisfaction of the same needs.*

---

[1] Called Gossen's First Law.

In accordance with experience it should be assumed that as personal income increases the number of new and different needs that people can satisfy also increases. This means that the number of wants felt depends on the sum of free decision. This may be presented on a graph.

On the horizontal axis we have the sum of free decisions S'' which is at the disposal of a single person. The vertical axis represents the sums S_i which, on the *average*, are earmarked by the person who has at his disposal the sum of free decisions S'', to satisfy need Q_i.

The bisector of the angle between the coordinate axes is the locus of points whose ordinates represent the maximum amount of expenditure for the satisfaction of needs at a given value of S''.

GRAPH 1.

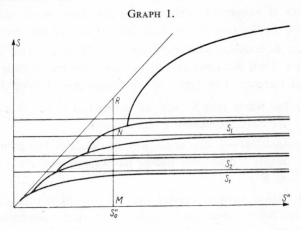

As S'' increases, new needs or groups of needs are satisfied. The sums spent on the satisfaction of needs Q_i are increasing functions of S'':

$$S_i = f(S'').$$

The functions are represented on the graph by curves. As the need is satisfied, as S'' increases, the sums S_i asymptotically approach straight lines parallel to the horizontal axis. The distance between these lines measured on the vertical axis represents the maximum amounts of sum S_i that are earmarked, on the average, by a single person for the satisfaction of certain needs. This means that if commodity C_1 satisfies need Q_1 then the total amount of this commodity that can be absorbed by the consumers, when the price of commodity C_1 is given and equals p_1, cannot exceed a certain constant value which depends upon the number of persons who possess sums of free decision S'' enabling them to satisfy need Q_1.

If the sum of free decision $S'' = S_0''$, then the ordinate of the point located on the bisector and determined by S_0'', represents the maximum amount that can be spent on the satisfaction of needs by a person whose sum of free decision $S'' = S_0''$ (the ordinate in question is represented on the graph by segment MR). The points of intersection of the ordinate with particular S_i curves determine the amounts of expenditures incurred on the average by the person possessing the sum of free decision $S'' = S_0''$ for the satisfaction of his needs.

Particular curves S_i which we shall call *want satisfaction curves*, or *want curves* run one above the other, according to the priority of wants, i.e. according to their intensity. Wants that we find it difficult not to satisfy are represented by curves located low on the graph. As S'' increases new needs appear; they are represented by curves located higher up.

The segment determined on the MR ordinate by two adjacent curves S_i and S_{i+1} reflects the average expenditure incurred for the satisfaction of need Q_{i+1} by a person for whom $S'' = S_0''$.

Segment MN represents the average total sum of expenditures for the satisfaction of the needs of a person for whom $S'' = S_0''$.

Segment $NR = MR - MN$ represents the average amount

saved during a certain period of time by a person for whom $S'' = S_0''$.

The knowledge of curves S_i is of great practical importance. These curves enable us to determine the expected amount of expenditures incurred by person Z for the satisfaction of particular needs depending upon the sums of free decisions at his disposal. They also enable us to determine the amount saved by person Z. This means that *knowing the distribution of personal income and curves S_i we know the character of social demand for goods and services.*

From the statistical point of view, curves S_i are regression curves reflecting the relationship between the expenditures for the satisfaction of particular needs and the sums of free decisions.

The determination of regression line parameters is the task of statistics. These parameters are determined on the basis of statistical material which should be as complete as possible, collected in the course of making statistical observations.

The analysis of the relationship between the amount of maintenance expenditures and the size of income was started by Engel. Analysing family budgets, he noticed that *the percentage share of maintenance expenditures decreases with an increase in income.* This relationship is known in the literature as the Engel–Schwabe Law (see [61], p. 47). Analysing the

GRAPH 2.

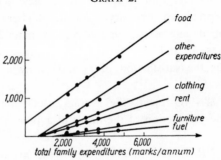

total family expenditures (marks/annum)

structure of family budgets, Engel derived an equation for the curves determining the stochastic relationship between the sum of maintenance expenditures and the size of income.

These curves are known as *Engel curves*. It is particularly worth noting that Engel curves may be approximated by *straight lines* with an accuracy sufficient for practical purposes. Engel curves shown on Graph 2 were determined by Allen and Bowley [3] on the basis of German statistical material for the years 1927–28.

As can easily be seen, we have here a case of a very clear *linear correlation*. The study of Engel curves has shown that they can be approximated by *linear* regression lines within their interval of validity[1].

Engel curves are a special case of want satisfaction curves. The term "want curves" was used by the author for the first time in study [30]. It is worth noting that since Engel's time a lot of attention has been devoted to the analysis of family budgets. On the basis of information derived from these budgets, research is being carried on concerning the relationship between the expenditures for the satisfaction of particular wants and the size of income. It has turned out that the terminology connected with these studies is not uniform. H. T. Davis in study [11] uses the term Engel curves for want curves. W. Winkler in study [61] objects to the use of this term and calls them Othmar Winkler's curves. Keynes [34] calls them consumption curves. A similar confusion developed with regard to the term used in the literature to describe the situation when consumption growth is slower than income growth. This economic phenomenon — besides the term "Engel's Law" — is also called a "declining propensity to consume". If, after Keynes, we denote consump-

---

[1] The interval of validity of a regression line is a numerical interval containing all measured values of the random variable of the sample appearing in the equation of regression as an argument

tion expenditures by C and income by Y we can express the relationship between consumption and income in the form of the following equation:

$$C = f(Y). \tag{1}$$

The derivative $\dfrac{dC}{dY}$ (see [34], p. 114) Keynes calls the marginal propensity to consume. On the same page of this work we read:

"Our normal psychological law that, when the real income of the community increases or decreases, its consumption will increase or decrease but not so fast, can, therefore, be stated... in a formally complete fashion... $\Delta Y_w > \Delta C_w$..."

The above statement has been quoted here to show that, regardless of certain differences of a secondary nature, the main idea expressed by Engel's Law and the "psychological law" of Keynes is the same. It is interesting to note that a similar idea is expressed by Gossen's First Law: "The intensity of a given need steadily decreases as it is satisfied until the level of saturation is reached" (see [26], p. 4).

Without becoming involved in a criticism of the conclusions derived by various economists from the laws quoted above we can say that all three laws express the following important economic truth, binding both in a capitalist and in a socialist economy: *individual wants weaken as they are satisfied.*

To conclude our considerations concerning numerous applications of want satisfaction curves we shall mention an interesting study by Wald [60] devoted to the problem of determining indifference surfaces. In his work Wald assumes that when three commodities x, y and z are considered the indifference function $W(x,y,z)$ is a second order polynomial of the type $W(x,y,z) = a_{00} + a_{01}x + a_{02}y + a_{03}z + a_{11}x^2 + a_{12}xy + a_{13}xz + a_{22}y^2 + a_{23}yz + a_{33}z^2$, where all the coefficients $a_{01}, a_{02},..., a_{33}$ can be found if the equations for the Engel curves are known.

The constant term a_{00}, however, cannot be determined. This constant term is not of great importance since it is necessary to know the indifference surface equation only in order to determine the equations of the indifference curves (isoquant equations), and these do not depend on a_{00}.

It follows that want curves, regardless of their names, are of fundamental importance to all contemporary mathematical economics. A number of important concepts and methods used in mathematical economics could certainly be used in the political economy of socialism. For this to happen, however, it is necessary to expand the studies of family budgets since the material they provide enables us to learn about the relationship between the amount of expenditure for the satisfaction of particular needs and the size of income. *Regression lines are a statistical way of expressing this relationship* (see 4.3., Example 1).

2.2.2. Income distribution curves

In the preceding section the relationship between the expenditures for the satisfaction of particular needs and the size of income has been described. This is undoubtedly one of the most important and interesting economic relationships. Naturally it does not appear in isolation but is causally related to other dependencies which form the whole, complex economic system.

For the full utilization of information supplied by want curves it is necessary to know the distribution of income. *By the distribution of income of the population we shall understand a statistical relationship between the size of income and the number of people in a given income bracket, or the relationship between the size of income and the frequency of its appearance.* These formulations are actually equivalent to one another; the formal difference between them consists in the fact that in one case we deal with frequencies and in the other with relative frequencies.

Below is an example of the distribution of income per person taken from the Statistical Yearbook for 1956 ([65], pp. 284–285). Table 1 shows the distribution of monthly earnings for September 1955.

TABLE 1

EMPLOYMENT ACCORDING TO MONTHLY EARNINGS FOR SEPTEMBER 1955

The number of employed persons in particular classes of gross earnings (in zlotys)

1	2	3	4	5	6	7	8	9
up to 400	401 to 600	601 to 800	801 to 1,000	1,001 to 1,500	1,501 to 2,000	2,001 to 2,500	2,501 to 3,000	over 3,000

in absolute figures (thousands)

181·9	625·1	1,017·8	979·2	1,516·3	565·9	200·2	76·4	57·4

For each particular wage group there is a corresponding figure showing the number of employees whose earnings fall into this class.

Table 2 also shows the distribution of monthly earnings in September 1955. It differs from Table 1 only in that relative frequencies have been substituted for frequencies.

A graph called a frequency histogram is a graphic presentation of the distribution. One condition that has to be fulfilled if a graph is to be drawn is that the class intervals of the frequency distribution be equal. Since the distribution shown in Table 1 has unequal class intervals then in order to draw a graph we have to calculate cumulative frequencies corresponding to particular class intervals of the frequency distribution:

1	2	3	4	5	6	7	8	9
up to 400	401 to 600	601 to 800	801 to 1,000	1,001 to 1,500	1,501 to 2,000	2,001 to 2,500	2,501 to 3,000	over 3,000
181·9	807·0	1,824·8	2,804·0	4,320·3	4,886·2	5,086·4	5,162·8	5,220·2

TABLE 2

EMPLOYMENT ACCORDING TO MONTHLY EARNINGS FOR
SEPTEMBER 1955

1	2	3	4	5	6	7	8	9
up to 400	401 to 600	601 to 800	801 to 1,000	1,001 to 1,500	1,501 to 2,000	2,001 to 2,500	2,501 to 3,000	over 3,000
relative frequencies								
3·5	12·0	19·5	18·8	29·0	10·8	3·8	1·5	1·1
cumulative frequencies								
3·5	15·5	35·0	53·8	82·8	93·6	97·4	98·9	100·0

Below is a graph showing cumulative frequencies based
on Table 2.

GRAPH 1.

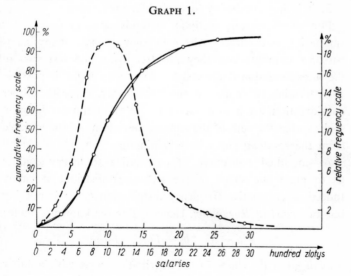

The cumulative frequency curve is shown on the graph as a broken line. This is the result of dividing statistical material into classes. If the classification of statistical observations and the preparation of frequency distributions could be avoided, the curve of cumulative frequencies would certainly be different. It would give a true picture of earnings in the month of September 1955 and would be free from distortions caused by the classification of statistical data. Treating the income of the population as a continuous variable, we can assume that the cumulative frequency curve would also be continuous. Its shape could be guessed in different ways. The simplest way would be to construct a polygon of relative frequency and to *smooth out by hand* the broken line obtained in this way. This is a really good and simple method but it is used rather reluctantly because:

1) it involves a certain degree of arbitrariness in drawing a curve;

2) it does not provide an equation of the curve;

3) it is not conducive to probability reasoning.

For these reasons analytic methods are preferred for smoothing out curves. Although they require many cumbersome computations they are free from the last two of the above-mentioned drawbacks. They also make it possible to determine the curve in the "best" way, i.e. with proper consideration given to a maximum or minimum condition — such as that the sum of the squared deviations of the variable from the *resultant* curve be a minimum.

A smoothed out curve of cumulative frequency enables us to guess the shape of the frequency distribution curve. Indeed, a cumulative frequency distribution curve is nothing but an *empirical distribution*. Hence, using the known formula:

$$P\{a < X < b\} = F(b) - F(a)$$

we can guess the shape of the distribution curve with a fairly good approximation. On Graph 1 the distribution curve is presented as a broken line.

An analysis of personal income, like an analysis of family budgets, should be based on current research data providing statistical material that can be used to determine particular want curves and the income distribution curve.

Let us denote by V the income per person, and by W_i the consumption per person of commodity A_i expressed in physical units, where i is the number of a commodity. In this case (V, W_i) is a two-dimensional random variable. Let $f = (v, w_i, t)$ denote the empirical distribution of this variable. This distribution changes in time, is a function of time. Let t_1, $t_2, \dots t_r \dots$ be consecutive moments in time and let $t_r - t_{r-1} = \Delta t$. For a sufficiently small interval Δt we can assume that *prices on the market are constant.* If for every given moment t_r supply S_i is greater than demand D_i and if the distribution is known for all i's then we have enough information to decide how demand changes with price. In a planned economy this would provide sufficient information for solving the problem of how to fix the volume of production to ensure market equilibrium. Unfortunately in practice this is not possible. There are too many goods and services to make it feasible to carry on statistical research on each of them in order to determine the function $f(v, w_i, t)$. The processing of statistical material pertaining to income and expenditures per person and a comprehensive analysis of this material require a lot of time and work. We can learn about only those relationships and dependencies which are of greatest importance to the national economy. The knowledge of the shape of the income distribution curve and of the want satisfaction curves is of special importance in a planned economy. Let us discuss this matter in greater detail. Let us assume that we know the shape of the income distribution curve and the shape of the want satisfaction curve for A (for example, A could

5*

be sugar). In this case for each size of income there are two corresponding figures: the number of persons in this income bracket or the relative frequency with which this income appears, and the average degree of satisfying need A, i.e. the average consumption of sugar by persons in this income bracket. On Graph 2 the relationship between the size of income and the average consumption of sugar per person is presented. Variable V is the argument and stands for the size of income; variable W denotes the average consumption of sugar per person. The dependence of W on V is described on the graph by the regression curve $\hat{w} = \varphi(v)$.

GRAPH 2.

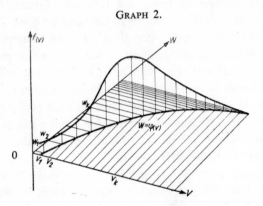

About a dozen points are distinctly marked on the curve. They are determined on the basis of statistical data. From these points perpendicular segments are drawn to the plane VOW. These segments represent the relative frequencies of the occurrence of particular magnitudes of income per person. Graph 2 is a three-dimensional graph. The relative frequencies shown on it are denoted by $f(v)$ and measured along the vertical axis.

It can be clearly seen from Graph 2 that if we know the shape of want satisfaction curve A and the shape of the income distribution curve we can easily determine both the average consumption per person of commodity A corresponding to a particular income group, and the total consumption of this commodity in particular groups. This enables the authorities to see to it — by using an appropriate price and wage control apparatus — that particular needs of the population are satisfied to a sufficiently high degree, with special consideration given to the protection of the interests of those in the lowest income groups.

If we assume that people in different income groups do not differ from each other with respect to the intensity of desire to satisfy want A, i.e. that people whose income is v_k and consumption is w_k would consume w_{k+1} if their incomes increased to v_{k+1} then it follows from Graph 2 that knowing the income distribution curve and the want satisfaction curve we can predict by how much the total consumption of commodity A will increase when the earnings of population group k grow from v_k to v_{k+1}. Denoting by Δ the total increase in the consumption of commodity A, and by N the total population we get the following equality:

$$\Delta = (w_{k+1} - w_k) \cdot f(v_k) \cdot N$$

(see Graph 2).

The knowledge of the want satisfaction curve and of the income distribution curve *allows us to predict* how the demand for a given commodity will change in consequence of changes in income. The latter are not the only cause of changes in demand. Besides income, price essentially affects the size of demand. In our considerations so far we have assumed that prices are constant. This was permissible since our analysis was limited to a sufficiently short period of time Δt. When research on income, consumption, prices, demand and supply is carried on continuously we can disregard those periods of time Δt during which a change in prices occurs, similarly as we proceed in analysing a function with a finite number of points of discontinuity. If economic research is conducted continuously then in every period $\varDelta t$, the incomes, average consumption and prices are known as is the *demand*. This is enough for the purpose of the *current* management of the economy. However, it is not enough for planning, or for *the scientific forecasting of the course of the economic processes in the future*. It is well known that for an economy to be in equilibrium it is required that at a given price of commodity A its supply be equal to the demand for it. Suppose that during a certain period of time the following situation prevails on the market: the supply of commodity A is small, the demand for it large and the price high. This price considerably exceeds the social cost of producing commodity A. This means that the *production of this commodity is very profitable*. If the economy is based on the principle of profitability this situation is bound to provide a stimulus to increasing production. An increase in production cannot occur instantaneously but requires a certain period of time. Thus the need for accurate scientific forecasting stems from the fact that the adjustment of supply to demand does not take place directly, as was the case in a primative economy, but through the market. As long as the market exists, so long will scientific forecasting be needed, regardless whether the market is in a capitalist or a socialist economy.

If a forecast of changes in demand is to be accurate we must know the relationship between demand and price as well as the relationship between demand and size of income. The knowledge of the relationship between demand and price allows us to answer the question: what will the probable demand be at a given price and what will the probable price be at a given demand? An accurate answer to this question is of great importance both in planning production and in fixing prices. To provide a correct answer it is necessary to know the demand curve. We shall now discuss these curves.

2.2.3. Demand curves

As we know, there is a distinct interdependence between price and demand in a free market economy; when the price rises — demand drops, when the price declines — demand increases. In this case

$$D = \psi(P), \qquad (1)$$

where P stands for the price of a commodity and D for the amount that can be sold at this price. Naturally, a functional description of complex relationships that exist between particular phenomena, or economic processes is always to some extent a scientific abstraction. In fact, the relationship between demand and price is not of a functional, but of a stochastic nature. This means that it is possible to express this relationship in mathematical language only by statistical methods. *Functions that are used in mathematical economics are a tool of learning only when they can be statistically verified.* All theoretical utterances about these functions are actually only scientific hypotheses until their correctness is checked by statistical methods. They become laws only after statistical verification.

We have made these comments because in many textbooks on economics no justification is given for representing the relationship between demand and price by a concave and monotonically downward sloping curve (see Graph 1).

GRAPH 1.

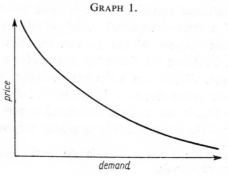

price

demand

Very little can be said *a priori* about the shape of the demand curve. All that we know is that it should fall as the price increases. The shape of the demand curve can be determined only by statistical methods. The demand curve, from a statistical point of view, is the regression line of D on P. This means that in order to express *the relationship between price and demand* in a functional language it is not enough to write down a function inverse to function (1), but that we have to find the other regression line, i.e. the *regression line* of P on D.

In a socialist economy in which the monetary commodity exchange system prevails, an analysis of demand not only does not lose its importance, but acquires new significance which is essentially different from the significance it has in a capitalist economy. The main purpose of analysing demand in a socialist economy is *to learn about the needs of the society and to adapt the production apparatus to the best possible satisfaction of these needs.*

Let us denote by W the average consumption per person of commodity A, by V income per person, and by P the price of commodity A. Between the random variable W and the random variables V and P there is a stochastic dependence. A certain defined value w corresponds to each pair of numbers (v,p). Suppose that as a result of statistical analysis we have obtained numerical material on the basis of which we have constructed a three-dimensional model of relationships between random variable W and random variables V and P (see Graph 2). Along the V-axis the centres of class intervals of the income distribution series are measured, and along the P-axis the prices that have been observed during study[1]. Along the W-axis the average consumption per person of commodity A is measured. The segments perpendicular to

---

[1] Segments on the V-axis are not in the same units as those representing price intervals.

plane *VOP* drawn from the middle of each square represent the volume of the average consumption per person of commodity *A* for various incomes and prices. The model would not be complete if it did not take into account the distribution of the random variable (*VPW*). Since in this model the values of the distribution function constitute a fourth variable we cannot draw the required number of coordinate axes in a three-dimensional space. We have overcome this difficulty by presenting on the graph the values of the empirical distribution function (i.e. frequencies) as squares of different areas located inside the squares of the chessboard. Let us note that by fixing the price and moving along the *V*-axis we find the relationship between the amount of the average consumption per person of commodity *A* and the size of income. This relationship, expressed by a regression line, is the want *satisfaction curve of commodity A*. By fixing the size of income and moving along the *P*-axis we find the relationship between the consumption per person of commodity *A* and the price. The regression curve describing this relationship is called the *demand curve*. If by *D* we denote the demand for commodity *A*, then

$$D(v,p) = W(v,p) \cdot f(v,p) \cdot N, \tag{2}$$

where $D(v,p)$ denotes the demand for *A* on the assumption that the price of this commodity is *p* and the income per person is *v*; similarly $W(v,p)$ denotes the average consumption per person of commodity *A* if $V = v$ and $P = p$, and if $f(v,p)$ denotes the frequency of random variable (V,P) at the point $(V = v, \ P = p)$. *N* stands for the total population.

The above graph presents the distribution of the the three-dimensional random variable (*VPW*). Suppose that this distribution is known. In this case, other things being equal, we also know the dependence of the demand for commodity *A* on both the size of income per person and the price of this

GRAPH 2.

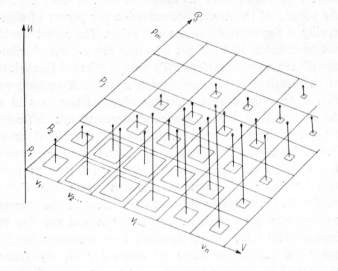

commodity. *Thus we have enough information to be able to adjust the supply to the demand for commodity A, i.e. to satisfy the economic equilibrium requirements.*

The knowledge of the distribution of the random variable (*VPW*) allows us to solve many important economic problems. Let us consider one of them. Suppose that the production and import potential does not permit us to saturate the market for commodity A to a degree sufficiently high to meet the demand for it at the constant price $P = p_0$. This means that, since the economic equilibrium requirements have been impaired, in addition to the rigid price p_0 fixed by the government, a new market equilibrium price p_1 (or rather a black market price) will appear. This price will shift on to the shoulders of the society the burden of maintaining speculators and smugglers and will constitute a temptation for dishonest employees of the socialized trade apparatus to hoard the scarce commodity. To prevent such a development, extremely harmful from an economic point of view, the State regulates the price of commodity *A* by trying to fix the price — at a given distribution of income per person — in such a way as *to ensure the sales of the stock of commodity A, and at the same time make revenues a maximum*. To regulate prices without causing undesirable social and economic results it is necessary to decide:

1) how to determine the equilibrium price of commodity *A*;
2) to what extent the demand for this commodity will be satisfied in population groups of different incomes per person.

We know that if at price $P = p_0$ the demand exceeds the supply, the equilibrium price p_1 will be higher than price p_0. The higher price p_1 will cause a drop in demand, thus adjusting the latter to the available supply. Of course, the drop in demand will occur because less well-to-do population groups will be forced to satisfy a smaller amount of their wants in consequence of the high price (too high a price of commodity *A*). Each forced renunciation of the satisfaction of social wants is an undesirable development from an economic point of view. However, it may sometimes be tolerated as a necessary evil if its social and economic consequences are not dangerous. They may be dangerous when *basic needs* are not satisfied. They should not be dangerous, however, when the restrictions affect the satisfaction of the needs for luxury goods. Naturally, if the interests of poorer people are to be protected, we have to know the process of satisfying wants in population groups of different income brackets, their respective purchasing powers and the market demand for commodity *A*.

Answers to these questions are facilitated by Graph 3.

In this graph we can see what the distribution of the amount *s* of commodity *A* would be at the price $P = p_j$. The areas of the bases of the parallelepipeds shown on the graph are

GRAPH 3.

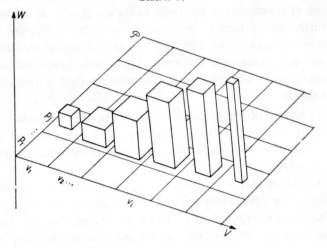

$f(v,p)$. The heights $W(v,p)$ of these parallelepipeds represent the average consumptions of commodity A, or, what amounts to the same thing, the average individual satisfactions of need A. Hence the volume of a parallelepiped, equal to the product $W(v_i p_j) \cdot f(v_i p_j)$, multiplied by the population number N, represents the demand for commodity A that exists in the population group whose income is $V = v_i$, when price $P = p_j$ (see formula 2). The total demand for commodity A equals the sum of the volumes of particular parallelepipeds multiplied by N. This means

$$D(\cdot p_j) = N \sum_i W(v_i p_j) \cdot f(v_i p_j). \tag{3}$$

It follows that, other things being equal, we can answer the questions concerning the size of the demand for commodity A when price $P = p$, the price of this commodity when the supply S of this commodity equals s, and the distribution of the amount s of commodity A among the population groups whose incomes are v_1, v_2, ... If we know the distribution of variable (VPW) we can solve the equations of the three regression surfaces. These equations are presented below in a general form

$$\hat{v} = g_1(p, w), \tag{4}$$

$$\hat{p} = g_2(v, w), \tag{5}$$

$$\hat{w} = g_3(v, p). \tag{6}$$

These formulae express in a functional way the relationships between three economic quantities: the average consumption per person of commodity A, the price of commodity A, and the average income per person. The determination of equations (4), (5) and (6) is very difficult in practice. This is due to the complex nature of economic phenomena which are interrelated by strong causal relations. In the course of observing economic phenomena we try to consider them in isolation. This approach always tends to diminish the accuracy of the results of observations and economic analysis because of the strength of causal relations existing between economic phenomena. In order to improve the accuracy, we must consider in the process of learning ever new relationships between the phenomena, trying to bring them into focus one by one, according to the diminishing strength of their influence.

If in equation (2) we substitute the expected value $\hat{w} = g_3(v,p)$ for $W(v,p)$ then the equation

$$\hat{d}(v, p) = g_3(v, p) \cdot f(v, p) \cdot N \tag{7}$$

will represent the expected size of the demand for commodity A on the assumption that income $V = v$ and price $P = p$.

Formula (7) expresses *explicitly* the dependence of demand on income and price. These two economic factors undoubtedly exert the greatest influence on the size of demand. *However, they are not the only factors.* If income and the price of commodity A are determined, the demand for it may change depending on changes in the prices of the complementary goods of, and substitutes for, commodity A. Since the determination of all the relationships of this type is practically impossible we either take into account only the most important relationships or content ourselves with an analysis of the relationship between demand, income and price.

Equation (5) shows the dependence of the price of commodity A on the average consumption per person of this commodity and on income.

In a free market economy the supply of commodity A depends on price.

Let us introduce new variables U, Y, Z, where U denotes sales revenues, Y costs and Z profit. In this case

$$U = X \cdot P \qquad (8)$$

and

$$U = Y + Z \qquad (9)$$

(symbol X denotes the volume of production).
At given values $P = p$, $Y = y$ and $Z = z$ the supply

$$s = \frac{y + z}{p}. \qquad (10)$$

In an economy governed by the principle of profitability *profit* is an economic factor providing an inducement to increase production. Of course, under these circumstances *production* should be increased until *profit reaches its maximum value*.

To decide how high the volume of production should be to obtain maximum profit *we have to know the relationship between costs and production*. The knowledge of this relationship is a condition for a rational management of production. It follows from the equation

$$p = \frac{y + z}{s} \qquad (11)$$

that at given values s and z the price of commodity A decreases when the cost of its production decreases. Since a drop in the price of commodity A results in an increase in the demand for it *the lowering of the cost of production leads to a better satisfaction of wants.*

2 2.4. Cost curves

As we know from mechanics, the ratio of the amount of energy received from a given machine to the amount of energy supplied to it is called the coefficient of efficiency and is denoted by the symbol η. Thus

$$\eta = \frac{E_1}{E_2},$$

where E_1 stands for the energy produced and E_2 for the energy used.

Graph 1 shows the curve for coefficient η as a function of variable E_1. This variable represents the output of energy produced by the machine studied.

GRAPH 1.

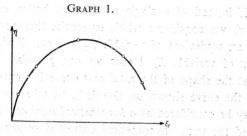

It follows from the characteristic shape of curve η that if the productive capacity of the machine is not fully utilized the coefficient of efficiency η is low. As production increases the efficiency of the machine rises and eventually reaches its maximum point. The abscissa of this point represents the optimum size of production $E_1 = E_{1_0}$. At this level of production the efficiency of the machine is the highest. If production increases beyond the optimum value E_{1_0} the efficiency of the machine decreases since it is overloaded and consequently operates under unfavourable conditions.

It follows from the shape of curve η that the curve representing the dependence of variable E_2 on variable E_1 must be a monotonically increasing curve.

This curve rises rapidly at first, then a little more slowly and then rapidly again (see Graph 2).

GRAPH 2.

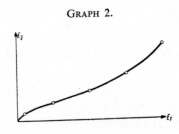

If instead of a single machine (a boiler, engine or generator) we consider a whole enterprise then production X will be an equivalent of variable E_1, and cost Y will be an equivalent of variable E_2. Hence we can postulate the hypothesis that the shape of the *total cost* curve is similar to the shape of the curve shown on Graph 2. In other words, this curve may be considered as *a hypothetical total cost curve*. We have used the term "hypothetical curve" since in reality both variable X (production) and variable Y (cost) are random variables. The joint distribution of variable (X, Y) is different for each enterprise. In order to learn about the shape of the regression line describing the relationship between cost and production we have to carry out appropriate statistical

GRAPH 3.

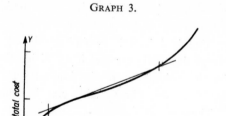

research in the enterprise which interests us. As we shall see later, the regression line is usually a *straight line*.

On Graph 3 the total cost curve is shown. On this graph we can also see a portion of a straight line which does not differ much from the curve between the points marked by two vertical dashes.

We shall denote the total cost by the symbol Y. On Graph 4 the hypothetical shape of curve Y is shown. It appears from the graph that costs are incurred even when the production equals zero. The amount of this cost is represented on the graph by the segment determined on the positive part of the Y-axis by the point of intersection of curve Y with this axis.

GRAPH 4. GRAPH 5.

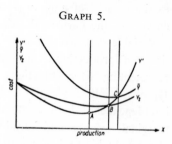

(According to Paulsen [43]).

6

These costs are known in literature under different names, e.g. *fixed costs*, or *independent costs*. The fixed cost is denoted on Graph 4 by the symbol Y_s. If we deduct the fixed cost from the total cost and if we divide the difference obtained by the volume of production we get the *variable cost* or *dependent cost*. The variable cost is denoted by the symbol Y_z. Thus

$$Y_z = \frac{Y - Y_s}{X}.$$

In a geometrical representation the variable cost is the tangent of angle α (see Graph 4).

By dividing the total cost by the volume of production we get the *average*, or *unit* cost which in Graph 5 is denoted by the symbol $\overline{Y}$. In this case

$$\overline{Y} = \frac{Y}{X}.$$

The average cost is equal to the tangent of angle β (Graph 4). If the total cost Y is a continuous function of the production and if at every point of a certain interval within which this function is determined, the derivative of this function is

$$Y' = \varphi(X)$$

then Y' is called the *marginal* cost. Marginal cost is equal to the tangent of angle γ between the line tangent to the curve and the horizontal axis (Graph 4).

Variable cost, average cost and marginal cost are all functions of production. On Graph 5 we can see three curves representing these functions. The cost curves shown on Graphs 4 and 5 are not only graphic presentations of the interdependence between total cost on the one hand, and marginal, average and variable costs on the other; they are also a valuable tool of research. On the basis of these curves we can make several important observations. Assuming that the hypothesis concerning the shape of the total cost curve is true, i.e. that:

1) the curve is located in the 1st quadrant of the coordinate system;

2) the ordinate of the curve at the point where the abscissa equals zero is not negative;

3) the curve is continuous within the whole interval of its validity and has a derivative at each point of this interval;

4) the curve has one point of inflexion separating the convex from the concave part;

the correctness of these observations follows directly from the graph. We can prove their validity in a formal way.

Observation 1. The minimum marginal cost is lower than the minimum variable cost which, in turn, is lower than the minimum average cost:

$$\min Y' < \min Y_z < \min \overline{Y}.$$

Observation 2. The minimum variable cost is determined by the point of intersection of the marginal cost curve with the variable cost curve (point *B* on Graph 5).

Observation 3. The minimum average cost is determined by the point of intersection of the marginal cost curve with the average cost curve (point *C* on Graph 5).

Cost curves allow us to find correct solutions to the problem of the "optimum production size".

Assuming that an economy is based on the principle of profitability the optimum size of production means the size at which *total profit is a maximum*. Some economists consider that the optimum size of production can be determined with the help of the unit cost curve. They maintain that the optimum level of production is one at which the average cost is a minimum and thus presumably profit is a maximum. In spite of its apparent correctness this statement is not true. We can easily prove the following:

THEOREM 1. Total profit reaches its maximum value when marginal revenue equals marginal cost, or, which amounts to the same thing, when marginal cost equals price.

Proof. Let U denote revenue, X — production, P — price, Y — cost and Z — profit. In this case

$$Z = U - Y.$$

If profit Z is to be a maximum it is necessary that

$$\frac{dZ}{dX} = \frac{dU}{dX} - \frac{dY}{dX} = 0.$$

i.e.

$$U' = Y'.$$

But

$$\frac{dU}{dX} = P.$$

Hence

$$U' = Y' = P.$$

GRAPH 6.

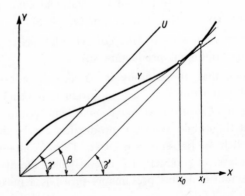

Graph 6 is a geometric representation of Theorem 1. It follows from the graph that profit attains its maximum value at $X = x_1$, and not at $X = x_0$.

This means that if we determine the volume of production in such a way as to minimize unit cost, the profit is less than it would be if the production were $X = x_1$. The correct optimum production size is obtained by using marginal cost and not average cost. Both Theorem 1 and its proof have been known in economics since the days of Cournot. This theorem is valid in a socialist economy if the principle of profitability is observed. So far this theorem has not been applied consciously (it is, perhaps, applied to planning production in such a way as to maximize profit at a given price, but this is done somewhat unintentionally, more on the basis of experience and intuition, than of theory). It seems that the chief reason for this attitude is the reluctance of economists to use mathematical and statistical methods of research in their professional work.

Cost analysis is indoubtedly one of the most important and difficult problems facing the economist. The lower the social cost of production the higher is the social productivity of labour and the better the satisfaction of the needs of the society. In economic literature the subject of costs occupies the most prominent position. The determination of the equation of a regression line which is an approximation to the total cost curve is a typical econometric problem. The practical aspect of this problem is sufficiently important to justify dealing with it in greater detail.

The human desire to satisfy wants induces people to produce such goods as will satisfy them. The production of these goods requires sacrifices on the part of the society; it requires labour power, materials, power and all those factors of production without which the production process would be impossible. The society is willing to make these sacrifices only because without them it is impossible to produce and thus to satisfy human needs. It follows that production is the only economic and social justification of the cost of production.

It follows from economic considerations that there should be an interdependence between costs and production. In mathematical economics it is assumed that cost is a function of production. The total cost curve is a geometrical representation of this function. The representation of the relationship between cost and production as a mathematical function is, of course, a scientific abstraction. In real life neither cost nor production is a variable in the general sense, but each is a random variable. We can learn about the interdependence between cost and production only by statistical research. The procedure leading to the knowledge of this interdependence has to follow a certain sequence. Each manufacturing enterprise keeps a record of cost and production. This record provides periodically — usually monthly — statistical data pertaining to the size of production and cost. If we denote production by X and cost by Y we can treat these quantities as the realization (x_i, y_i) $(i = 1,2,..., n)$ of the two-dimensional random variable (X,Y). A point on a plane corresponds to each pair of numbers (x_i, y_i). A collection of such points may be regarded as a sample selected from an infinite general population. If it is true that there is an interdependence between cost and production and if production and cost records are properly kept, the distribution of points on the scatter diagram will show a trend. The regression line, being a statistical representation of this trend, is a functional way of expressing the interdependence between cost and production.

It is especially worth noting that, as numerous studies have shown, the regression line describing the relationship between cost and production is usually a straight line. Let us quote a few opinions on this subject. Falewicz (page 61 of

his book quoted here) says: "In spite of the fact that theoretically the line best representing the relationship between
cost and production — if it could be established for all possible sizes of production from 0 to the highest that the capacity
of the enterprise permits — would be a curve of an equation
of a high — probably not less than 3rd — degree, in practice,
when it is possible to study this relationship only within certain limits of production size, we can assume, with a sufficiently high degree of accuracy that it can be represented by
a *straight line*".

And here is what Tinbergen has to say: "It has been established that in many industries the shape of the curve of total
cost with respect to the volume of production can generally
be represented by a straight line". Similar opinions are expressed by Dean [12], Lyle [37] and many other statisticians
who have studied the interdependence between cost and
production. Very characteristic and to the point is a comment
by Tintner. On page 49 of his book [57] we read: "It is remark-
able that (in the relevant interval covered by the data) the
total cost of making steel, seems to be a linear function of the
amount of product. Hence the marginal cost is constant.
The importance of this fact of constant short-run marginal
cost discovered by all investigators of statistical cost functions contradicts the *a priori* assumptions of the economists."

We have quoted the above opinions in order to show that
in practice the regression line describing the relationship
between cost and production is a straight line. This is of great
importance since the determination of the linear regression
parameters is relatively easy and, therefore, a statistical analysis of the relationship between cost and production could
and should be made widely known.

2.2 5. Time curves

Time series constitute a wide field for applications of regression theory. It is well known that a trend is one of the characteristics of a time series. The notion of trend is interpreted in the literature in a variety of ways. Below we describe two generally accepted interpretations.

Interpretation I. The following time series is given

$$x_1, \; x_2, \; ..., \; x_t,...$$

where t assumes integer values. An illustration of a time series is provided by the corn crop yields in the USSR in 1922–1934.

TABLE 1

CROP YIELDS IN THE USSR

Year	Yields in metric quintals per hectare
1922	7·6
1923	7·2
1924	6·2
1925	8·3
1926	8·2
1927	7·6
1928	7·9
1929	7·5
1930	8·5
1931	8·7
1932	7·0
1933	8·8
1934	8·5

(see [41], p. 171).

The statistical data of Table 1 are shown on Graph 1. The broken line on this graph is called a *time curve*. It shows various irregular breaks which are a result of random factors. These breaks in the time curve not only do not help in the process of learning, but on the contrary, make it difficult to detect the influence of the regular factor which causes crop yields per hectare to show a tendency to increase.

GRAPH 1.

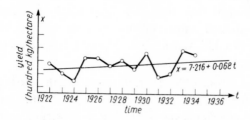

According to the first interpretation a *trend is a line express-ing a general tendency in the shape of a time curve.* A trend line is determined by the elimination of random oscillations from the time curve. The parameters of the trend line are obtained by appropriate statistical methods, e.g. the moving average method, or the method of least squares. This inter-pretation of trend is accepted by O. Lange in his textbook on statistics [35] in which he writes: "Analysing time series we notice that they show a certain development tendency" (p. 181). And further on: "Table 46 gives yields in metric quintals per hectare in the USSR in 1922–1934; these data are shown on Graph 46[1]. A development tendency can be clearly seen. The yield per hectare fluctuates from year to year but on the whole there is, undoubtedly, an increase in yield... A development tendency may be emphasized by a procedure called the *smoothing out* of a time series" (p. 182).

In this interpretation a trend line is a regression II line; by a visual inspection of the time series we select a family

---

[1] See Table 1, Graph 1.

of approximation functions and determine the parameters
of one of the functions belonging to this family. The curve
of this function is the *trend line*. The role of the trend line in
this interpretation is to smooth out the time curve. The value
of the trend line as a tool of learning is much smaller than
the value of the regression I line. In an analysis of the relationship between two random variables X and Y when both
are independent from time, the regression I line assigns conditional expected values of one variable to any values of
the other variable. When we deal with a time series there are
no conditional expected values involved.

Trend is a *smoothed out time curve*. In the first interpretation, trend can be used only *to describe* a time series, but
it cannot constitute the basis for a prediction concerning
the development of a stochastic process in the future. Even
the most careful extrapolation is not permissible.

Interpretation II. The values of a time series are a realization
of a certain stochastic process. This process may be subject
to some *law* which can be described by an appropriate mathematical function. The nature of this law, and consequently
the shape of the function, are known. The parameters of the
function, however, are not known. They can be estimated by
statistical methods on the basis of the statistical material
contained in the time series. In this interpretation *the trend
line is a geometric presentation of the function which is known,
a priori, to be a mathematical expression of a law governing
the stochastic process under consideration.*

This interpretation often leads one astray and results in
mathematical formalism. The law governing a stochastic process is rarely known *a priori*[1]. Hence a temptation to proceed
in the following way: on the basis of the visual inspection of

---

[1] In economic applications this law is sometimes known in the statistical quality control of production.

the shape of a time curve we select an appropriate approximation function and then argue "theoretically" that this curve expresses, in fact, a "law" governing the realization of a stochastic process. Such a temptation is particularly strong when a time curve shows only minor fluctuations, like the curve shown on Graph 2. It would seem that this kind of procedure is too obviously against common sense to be used. This is not so, however. O. Lange, in his book mentioned above, quotes two examples of an improper application of a logistic curve to smoothing out a time series. In both cases a logistic curve was used not only because it "fitted" well to the statistical material but primarily because it allegedly expressed the "law of growth" which can be presented in a mathematical form as a differential equation:

$$\frac{dx}{dt} = x(a-x)\ g(t), \qquad (0 < x < a),$$

where a is a constant called the "level of saturation".

The application of this equation to the analysis of the trend line is deprived of all economic justification. Both cases cited by Lange are examples of mathematical formalism; he emphasizes this fact very strongly.

The equation of a logistic curve is the integral of the differential equation mentioned above and presumably expressing the "law of growth".

One of the examples given in Lange's book comes from "Theory of Econometrics" by H. T. Davis, who also wrote "The Analysis of Economic Time Series". The latter book prompted M. G. Kendall to express the following short but pointed opinion: "Davis's book on 'The Analysis of Economic Time Series' (1941) contains a great deal of interesting material but should not be read uncritically" (see [33], p. 437).

Linear regression

GRAPH 2.

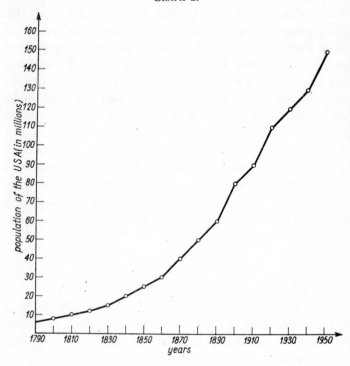

(see [64]).

It might be worth while to mention here a very pertinent comment on the subject of formalism by A. Hald:

"The logistic curve has been frequently used to illustrate the growth of 'populations' (cells, human populations, telephone subscribers, etc.), the development of business transactions between different countries, education of persons in various manual and mental accomplishments, etc. Regarding most of these applications it may be said that the *theoretical* analysis of the growth process in hand is so uncertain that it is doubtful whether or not the process is governed by a differential equation such as (20.7.2)[1], wherefore application of the logistic curve is mainly based on its descriptive properties. The results of the extrapolations regarding population figures, production, etc., which have been carried out on this basis should therefore be regarded with great scepticism" [28][2].

J. M. Keynes expresses his opinion on the matter very frankly:

"Too large a proportion of recent 'mathematical' economics are mere concoctions, as imprecise as the initial assumptions they rest on, which allow the author to lose sight of the complexities and interdependencies of the real world in a maze of pretentious and unhelpful symbols" ([34], p. 298). It would appear from the above quotations that if there are economists who use mathematics improperly, there also are those who see and criticize their mistakes.

The more correct of the two interpretations of trend described above is the first. It follows from the definition given on p. 88, that from a formal point of view the trend line can be considered as a regression II line. All those who prefer the first interpretation of the trend line agree on this. However, there is one doubt. The regression II line is a function $g(x)$ for which

$$E[Y-g(x)]^2 = \text{minimum} \tag{1}$$

(see p. 36). With respect to the time series $x_1, x_2, ..., x_t ...$ formula (1) will assume the following form:

$$E[X-g(t)]^2 = \text{minimum}, \tag{2}$$

---

[1] i.e. by equation:

$$\frac{dx}{dt} = \begin{cases} g(t), \\ x \cdot g(t), \\ (a-x)g(t), & (0 < x < a), \\ x(a-x)g(t), & (0 < x < a). \end{cases}$$

[2] A. Hald: *Statistical Theory with Engineering Applications*, New York, 1952, p. 661.

where $g(t)$ is the symbol of the trend equation. Formula (2) states that the trend is a function of time $g(t)$ for which the mathematical expectation of squared deviations of the values of the time series from the values of this function at moments $t = 1,2,...$ is a minimum. The doubt mentioned above is due to the fact that it is not really known exactly how to interpret the notion of mathematical expectation with respect the random variable dependent upon time. With reference to a random variable which is independent of time, mathematical expectation is a distribution parameter of this variable. This parameter is a *number*. The situation is different when the random variable *depends* on time. In this case its distribution depends on time and consequently also the parameters of this distribution depend on time, *are functions of time*. Naturally this case is *not covered by the definition of the mathematical expectation of a random variable* independent of time. This means that if the trend is understood as a regression II line of a random variable correlated to time then there are certain aspects that require explanation. It should be stressed that the problem of the definition of a trend is, so far, an open problem in the literature on statistics. For instance, Hald [28] mentions a textbook by Kendall [33] in the bibliography of studies related to time series. Indeed, this textbook can be considered as the most important one as far as time series are concerned because of the amount of space and attention given to this subject. However, even Kendall does not give a definition of a trend that is free from the reservations mentioned above (see [33], p. 371). This fact has prompted the author to attempt to formulate such a definition. It is given in 6.1.

2.2.6. *Techno-economic curves*

Correlation analysis finds many applications in different branches of technology where it is often necessary to discover relationships between various random variables. Among such relationships are: the relationship between the amount of gas or liquid sucked in by a suction pump and the degree of vacuum created in the pump, expressed in percentages; the relationship between the durability of alloys used for heat resistors and the temperature in which they operate; the relationship between the hardness of steel used for tool manufacturing and temperature or carbon content, etc.

There is no need to give further examples of the applications of correlation analysis to technological research. They are numerous and increase almost every day. It should be emphasized that studies on relationships in the field of technique very often have an important *economic* aspect in addition to a technical aspect. For instance, if some changes have been introduced in a technological process (i.e. in the process of manufacturing scarce goods) in consequence of technological research, these changes may, and usually do, have economic as well as technical effects. From an economic point of view these effects may be positive, neutral, or negative. The criterion for this type of classification is found in production costs.

Let us discuss the already-mentioned relationship between the durability of heat resistant alloys and the temperature in which they are used. This type of research is conducted in connection with a search for the most durable alloys. In electrical engineering various alloys are used: constantan, manganin, nickeline, nichrome, chromel, alumel, kanthal and others. Each of these alloys has a different durability, different resistance to high temperatures, changes in the frequency of heating, cooling, etc. Depending on the technical requirements, one or another type of alloy is used. In making a choice economic consequences have to be taken into consideration. Some alloys can be produced at home and others have to be imported; for some of them the raw materials are available at home; for some they are not. Costs of production are different for each alloy. The more durable alloys are usually more expensive. It follows that studies of the relationship between the durability of the alloy and temperature are of interest not only to the technician but also to the economist.

All examples of statistical relationships which have both *technological* and *economic* aspects we shall call *techno-economic relationships*. The curves which are a graphic representation of these relationships we shall call *techno-economic curves*. An interesting example of techno-economic curves is presented on Graph 1, taken from a study by Vernon L. Smith (see [53])[1].

GRAPH 1.

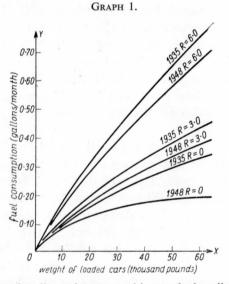

The regression lines shown on this graph describe the relationship between the consumption of fuel and the weight of a car together with its load. Number *R* is a measure of the

---

[1] See also 3.2.2., Example 2.

slope of the road (the slope coefficient). It is a fraction expressing the increase in height in feet per 100 feet of the lenght of the road. It can be seen from the graph how the consumption of fuel has decreased in consequence of technical improvements. The greater the value of R the smaller is the drop in the consumption of fuel. The relationship between fuel consumption and the weight of the car with a load is a technical problem, but its economic consequences are so clear and far reaching, that no comments are required. The regression curves shown on the graph can be used as a basis for setting fuel consumption *norms*. Much has been written in literature about the uselessness of "statistical" norms and the necessity of replacing them by "technical" norms. It can be seen from the above example that without the help of statistics (in this case correlation analysis) it would be difficult to set a technical norm.

3. ESTIMATING LINEAR REGRESSION PARAMETERS

3.1. General remarks about methods of estimating

There are several methods of estimating the parameters of a general population on the basis of statistical data supplied by a random sample of the population. The most important are: *the maximum likelihood method, the minimum variance method, the minimum χ^2 method, and the method of least squares*. So far, only the method of least squares has been used in regression theory because of its many advantages. This method is *easier to comprehend* than the others since it requires only knowledge of how to find the maximum or minimum of a function by differential calculus, and it is not necessary to know mathematical statistics. The method of least squares is very *general*. It may provide solutions in cases when other methods have failed. For both these reasons the method of least squares is known by astronomers and surveyors, physicists and biologists, technicians and economists. Since a basic knowledge of calculus is necessary to learn the method of least squares, it is used almost exclusively by scientists. Practical workers rarely use it.

The method of least squares has a very valuable formal quality, *important in cases of linear regression*. There is a theorem known as the *Markoff Theorem* [8] which states that estimates obtained by this method *are consistent, unbiased and most efficient*. In this theorem it is not assumed that the distribution of random variables is normal, or even that these variables are independent.

In spite of these unquestionable advantages of the method of least squares, there are two reasons why we here propose a new method of estimating regression parameters besides the method of least squares. Until it is finally given a name we shall call it *the two-point method*. However, it should be understood that this is only a temporary term. In cases of linear regression the two-point method also provides consistent and unbiased estimates of regression parameters, but

1) computations of the values of estimates are much easier than those required in the method of least squares, and

2) to learn the two-point method it is not necessary to know the calculations for maxima and minima required in the method of least squares.

The efficiency of the estimates obtained by the two-point method is a little lower than the efficiency of the estimates obtained by the method of least squares, but when a sample is large this consideration does not carry great weight. The important advantages that are gained by the introduction of the two-point method in the theory of estimating linear regression parameters consist, first of all, in the fact that this method is conducive to the *popularization of regression and correlation theory* among practical workers. This is of particular importance in economic research. In Chapter 2 we have discussed the most important applications of regression and correlation to economic research. These applications are diverse and important to the economy. However, they will be of real service in expediting the control of economic processes only when correlation analysis becomes a handy tool of economic analysis, known and willingly used by those engaged in economic activities. The main obstacle to popularizing regression and correlation methods among economists is the undoubtedly too high requirement of mathematical knowledge for the determination of regression parameters by the classical method[1]. The two-point method is, to a large extent, free of these difficulties. Let us hope that many people, after they learn the two-point method and see the advantages in the application of statistical methods to studies of the relationships between random variables, will make an effort to improve their knowledge and gradually to master the classical method:

3.2. Estimating linear regression parameters by the method of least squares

3.2.1. The derivation of formulae. Examples

All our further considerations concerning the two-dimensional variable (X,Y) will be based on the following assumptions [28][2]:

1) the conditional distributions of variable Y, corresponding to any values of variable X, are normal distributions;

2) the regression line of Y on X in a general population is a straight line with the equation

$$\hat{y} = \alpha x + \beta,$$

where α and β are constant parameters;

3) the conditional variance $V(Y|X = x)$ is a constant;

4) points (x_i, y_i) $(i = 1,2,...,n)$ drawn for the sample, where n is the size of the sample, are stochastically independent.

Let us denote by Ω a two-dimensional general population. The random variable (X,Y) is defined by the elements of this population. From population Ω we draw a random sample ω comprising n items.

---

[1] i.e. the method of least squares.

[2] A. Hald: *Statistical Theory with Engineering Applications*, New York, 1952, p. 528.

Problem. On the basis of the data from sample ω, estimate the parameters α and β of the regression line $\hat{y} = \alpha x + \beta$ in the general population Ω.

This type of problem is usually solved by the method of least squares. Let us denote by a and b the estimates — obtained from the sample — of the unknown parameters α and β in Ω. In order to determine the values of these estimates we have to minimize the expression

$$\sum_{i=1}^{n} (y_i - ax_i - b)^2.$$

After simple transformations (see 1.2.7.) we get a set of normal equations:

$$\sum_{i=1}^{n} x_i y_i - a \sum_{i=1}^{n} x_i^2 - b \sum_{i=1}^{n} x_i = 0,$$

$$\sum_{i=1}^{n} y_i - a \sum_{i=1}^{n} x_i - b = 0.$$

Solving them with respect to a and b we obtain

$$b = \bar{y} - a\bar{x}, \qquad (1)$$

$$a = \frac{\sum_{i=1}^{n} (x_i - \bar{x})(y_i - \bar{y})}{\sum_{i=1}^{n} (x_i - \bar{x})^2}. \qquad (2)$$

In formula (1) $\bar{x}$ and $\bar{y}$ are *arithmetic means of the sample,* i.e.

$$\bar{x} = \frac{1}{n} \sum_{i=1}^{n} x_i, \qquad \bar{y} = \frac{1}{n} \sum_{i=1}^{n} y_i. \qquad (3)$$

The *equation of the regression line of the sample* assumes the form:

$$\tilde{y} = ax + b. \qquad (4)$$

Let us denote further

$$s_1 = \sqrt{\frac{1}{n} \sum_{i=1}^{n} (x_i - \bar{x})^2}, \quad s_2 = \sqrt{\frac{1}{n} \sum_{i=1}^{n} (y_i - \bar{y})^2}. \quad (5)$$

These are *standard deviations of variables X and Y of the sample.*

$$c(xy) = \frac{1}{n} \sum_{i=1}^{n} (x_i - \bar{x})(y_i - \bar{y}). \quad (6)$$

This is the *covariance of the sample.*

In this case the regression parameters of Y on X can be found in the following way:

$$b_{20} = \bar{y} - a_{21}\bar{x}, \quad (7)$$

$$a_{21} = \frac{c(xy)}{s_1^2}. \quad (8)$$

It is not difficult to notice the similarity of formulae (7) and (8) to formulae (6) and (8) from 1.2.7.

Similarly for the regression of X on Y we have

$$b_{10} = \bar{x} - a_{12}\bar{y}, \quad (9)$$

$$a_{12} = \frac{c(xy)}{s_2^2}. \quad (10)$$

Parameters a_{21} and a_{12} we shall call *regression coefficients of the sample.*

In case of the regression of Y on X the *standard error of the estimate in the sample* — by analogy to formula (16) in 1.2.7. — is defined as follows:

$$s_{21} = \sqrt{s_2^2 - a_{21}c(xy)}. \quad (11)$$

Similarly, for the regression of X on Y:

$$s_{12} = \sqrt{s_1^2 - a_{12}c(xy)}. \quad (12)$$

The sample *correlation coefficient r* is an estimate of the correlation coefficient of the general population Ω. We shall define coefficient r by the formula

$$r^2 = a_{12} \cdot a_{21}, \tag{13}$$

by analogy to formula (6), 1.2.8.

We shall illustrate by an example the method of determining numerical values of the estimates of regression line parameters obtained by the method of least squares.

Example 1. Analyse the relationship between the consumption of compressed air Y and the amount of coal X extracted from mine Z.

The relationship between the amount used and the volume of production expressed in the form of increased input consumption in consequence of increased production is a result of a causal relation existing between input consumption and production; the only economic reason for increased input consumption is increased production. The amount of consumption is influenced not only by the volume of production, but also by secondary causes such as differences in attitude toward work among employees during working hours, changes in the condition of equipment, differences in the quality of raw materials, damages to machines and many others. As a result of these causes, the relationship between the amount of input consumption and the volume of production appears to be of a stochastic nature.

The consumption of compressed air is related to the use of machines and technical equipment needed primarily for the extraction of coal. The most typical are: hammer drills, drills and punching machines. The characteristic feature of such machines is that at the moment they stop operating the consumption of air used as operating power also stops. In this respect they are different from other machines driven by other sources of energy like steam or oil; these use up substantial amounts of energy during their unproductive work.

The monthly data on the volume of coal production and the amount of compressed air used up cover a period of three years. Both production and consumption are expressed in physical and not monetary units. This eliminates the disturbances which might appear in the relationship as a result of price changes. The data on which the analysis of the relationship between the consumption of compressed air and the production of coal is based are shown in Table 1.

TABLE 1

CONSUMPTION OF COMPRESSED AIR AND THE PRODUCTION
OF COAL IN A MINE

Month	1949		1950		1951	
	x	y	x	y	x	y
1	112	18·5	102	18·1	96	16·2
2	98	17·1	93	15·4	94	15·2
3	118	18·4	100	17·9	97	15·4
4	104	17·6	100	17·4	83	14·3
5	105	17·7	104	18·1	84	14·5
6	104	18·5	104	18·5	103	17·0
7	102	18·7	104	19·5	97	16·2
8	108	18·8	108	19·2	101	17·1
9	111	19·2	101	17·3	104	18·5
10	107	18·4	103	19·5	102	17·2
11	105	17·4	110	19·1	107	18·3
12	91	15·3	106	18·1	94	17·5

x — the extraction of coal in thousands of tons per month,
y — the consumption of air in millions of cubic metres per month.

The corresponding *scatter diagram* is shown on Graph 1. A graph should always be made before the equations of the regression lines are computed, because it supplies initial

GRAPH 1.

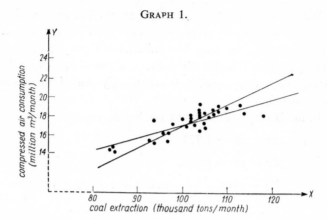

coal extraction (thousand tons/month)

information about the nature of the relationship between the variables studied. This information enables us: 1) to form an opinion whether the relationship between the variables is strong or weak, 2) to choose a mathematical function to serve as an approximation to the relationship between the variables. In Graph 1 the relationship between the consumption of compressed air and the extraction of coal is presented. Both regression lines are shown; their equations are computed below. The distribution of points in the graph indicates a linear trend. We can see from the graph that the correlation in this case is positive since an increase in one variable is accompanied by an increase in the other. The correlation between the variables studied can be considered fairly strong. This statement is based on observations indicating that the direction and magnitude of changes in consumption and production *generally* correspond to one another. In other words, when production increases, consumption also increases and the greater the increase in production, the greater the increase in consumption and vice versa, in most cases a drop in production causes a drop in consumption and the greater the former, the greater the latter.

We have completed reading the graph. Let us now determine the parameters of the regression line. To calculate a_{21}, a_{12}, b_{20} and b_{10} we have to find $\Sigma(x-\bar{x})(y-\bar{y})$; $\Sigma(x-\bar{x})^2$; $\Sigma(y-\bar{y})^2$; (see (7), (8), (9), (10)). Computations involved in determining these quantities are usually placed in a table (see Table 2).

In the last row of the table, marked Σ, we read:

$$\Sigma(x-\bar{x})^2 = 1,774,$$

$$\Sigma(y-\bar{y})^2 = 65 \cdot 14,$$

$$\Sigma(x-\bar{x})(y-\bar{y}) = 280 \cdot 24 - 1 \cdot 9 = 278 \cdot 34,$$

$$\Sigma x = 3,672, \text{ hence } \bar{x} = 102,$$

$$\Sigma y = 630 \cdot 0, \text{ hence } \bar{y} = 17 \cdot 5.$$

Having the above data we calculate the parameters of both regression lines:

$$a_{21} = \frac{\Sigma(x-\bar{x})(y-\bar{y})}{\Sigma(x-\bar{x})^2} = \frac{278 \cdot 34}{1,774} = 0 \cdot 156.$$

In order to determine the dimensions of parameter a_{21}, we insert into the formula

$$\frac{\Sigma(x-\bar{x})(y-\bar{y})}{\Sigma(x-\bar{x})^2} \text{ dimension}$$

x — thousands of tons of coal per month,
y — millions of cubic metres of air per month.
We obtain

$$\frac{\text{thous. tons of coal/month} \times \text{mln.m}^3 \text{ of air/month}}{\text{thous. tons of coal/month} \times \text{thous. tons of coal/month}}$$

$$= \frac{\text{thous. m}^3 \text{ of air}}{\text{tons of coal}},$$

i.e.:

$$a_{21} = 0 \cdot 156 \frac{\text{thous. m}^3 \text{ of air}}{\text{tons of coal}} = 156 \frac{\text{m}^3 \text{ of air}}{\text{tons of coal}}.$$

TABLE 2

METHOD OF LEAST SQUARES APPLIED TO TABLE 1

No	x	y	$x-\bar{x}$ +	$x-\bar{x}$ −	$y-\bar{y}$ +	$y-\bar{y}$ −	$(x-\bar{x})^2$	$(y-\bar{y})^2$	$(x-\bar{x})(y-\bar{y})$ +	$(x-\bar{x})(y-\bar{y})$ −
1	114	18·5	12		1·0		144	1·00	12·00	
2	98	17·1		4		0·4	16	0·16	1·60	
3	118	18·4	16		0·9		256	0·81	1·44	
4	104	17·6	2		0·1		4	0·01	0·20	
5	103	17·2	1			0·3	1	0·09		0·3
6	104	18·0	2		0·5		4	0·25	1·00	
7	104	18·5	2		1·0		4	1·00	2·00	
8	108	18·8	6		1·3		36	1·69	7·80	
9	113	19·4	11		1·9		121	3·61	20·90	
10	107	18·4	5		0·9		25	0·81	4·50	
11	105	17·4	3			0·1	9	0·01		0·3
12	93	15·5		9		2·0	81	4·00	18·00	
13	102	18·1	0	0	0·6		0	0·36	0	0
14	93	15·4		9		2·1	81	4·41	18·90	
15	100	17·9		2	0·4		4	0·16		0·8
16	102	17·6	0	0	0·1		0	0·01	0	0
17	104	18·1	2		0·6		4	0·36	1·20	
18	104	18·5	2		1·0		4	1·00	2·00	
19	104	19·5	2		2·0		4	4·00	4·00	
20	108	19·2	6		1·7		36	2·89	10·20	
21	101	17·3		1		0·2	1	0·04	0·20	
22	103	18·5	1		1·0		1	1·00	1·00	
23	110	19·1	8		1·6		64	2·56	12·80	
24	106	18·1	4		0·6		16	0·36	2·40	
25	96	16·2		6		1·3	36	1·69	7·80	
26	94	15·2		8		2·3	64	5·29	18·40	
27	97	15·4		5		2·1	25	4·41	10·50	
28	85	14·3		17		3·2	289	10·24	54·40	
29	84	14·5		18		3·0	324	9·00	54·00	
30	103	17·0	1			0·5	1	0·25		0·5
31	97	16·2		5		1·3	25	1·69	6·50	
32	101	17·0		1		0·5	1	0·25	0·50	
33	104	18·5	2		1·0		4	1·00	2·00	
34	102	17·8	0	0	0·3		0	0·09	0	0
35	107	18·3	5		0·8		25	0·64	4·00	
36	94	17·5		8	0	0	64	0	0	0
Σ	3,672	630·0	93	93	19·3	19·3	1,774	65·14	280·24	1·9
									278·34	

$\bar{x} = 102, \quad \bar{y} = 17·5.$

We calculate b_{20}:

$$b_{20} = \bar{y} - a_{21}\bar{x} = 17,500,000 \text{ m}^3 \text{ of air/month} -$$

$$- 156 \frac{\text{m}^3 \text{ of air}}{\text{tons of coal}} \cdot 102,000 \text{ tons of coal/month}$$

$$= 17,500,000 \text{ m}^3 \text{ of air/month} - 15,912,000 \text{ m}^3 \text{ of air/month}$$

$$= 1,588,000 \text{ m}^3 \text{ of air/month}.$$

Thus the equation determining the average consumption of air in relation to the extraction of coal has the following form:

$$\bar{y} = 1,588,000 \text{ m}^3 \text{ of air/month} + 156 \frac{\text{m}^3 \text{ of air}}{\text{tons of coal}} x.$$

The equation may be called *a characteristic of consumption* of compressed air. For any data concerning production, providing they are taken from the interval of validity of the function, this equation provides the estimate of the average consumption of air for a given volume of production. The interval of validity of the function lies between the lowest and the highest value of the random variable appearing in the regression line equation as an argument. In our example this interval is:

$$(84,000 \text{ tons, } 118,000 \text{ tons}).$$

The regression line is a geometric representation of the *input consumption characteristic*; after Falewicz, we shall call it *the line of normal input consumption*.

To satisfy their needs, people have to produce various goods.

"The labour process, resolved into its simple elementary factors, is as we have seen, purposive activity carried on for the production of use-values, for the fitting of natural substances to human wants; it is the general condition requisite for effecting an exchange of matter between man and nature; it is the condition perennially imposed by nature upon human life..." ([38], p. 177). Thus, labour is a tribute that man pays to nature for her products. He tries for natural reasons to minimize this tribute; he tries to achieve his economic aims with the minimum of effort. This principle lies at the basis of all economic activities.

We shall introduce the following definition of *efficiency of the enterprise*. By the efficiency we shall understand the totality of the activities of the enterprise aimed at the attainment of its economic objectives with the least outlay both in the form of "living" and "stored up" labour. The control of the efficiency of a socialist enterprise is one of the most important tasks of socialist economics. *The normal input consumption line is an effective tool of such control.* This line determines the average, the most probable, and thus the *normal* amount of input consumption corresponding to different levels of production. If the consumption is lower than "normal" we can say that the enterprise has successfully raised its efficiency; if it is higher — it means that the enterprise has failed in its efforts to increase its efficiency[1].

Let us compute the values of the regression parameters of X on Y. It follows from formulae (9) and (10) and from Table 2 that

$$a_{12} = \frac{278 \cdot 34}{65 \cdot 14} = 4 \cdot 27;$$

dimension a_{12}:

$$\frac{\text{mln. m}^3/\text{month} \times \text{thous. tons/month}}{\text{mln. m}^3/\text{month} \times \text{mln. m}^3/\text{month}}$$

$$= \frac{\text{thous. tons}}{\text{mln. m}^3} = 0 \cdot 001 \frac{\text{tons}}{\text{m}^3}.$$

---

[1] An extensive discussion of applications of linear regression to the economic control of an enterprise can be found in studies [23], [37].

Hence

$$a_{12} = 4\cdot27 \cdot 0\cdot001 \frac{\text{tons of coal}}{\text{m}^3 \text{ of air}} = 0\cdot00427 \frac{\text{tons of coal}}{\text{m}^3 \text{ of air}}.$$

In this case

$$b_{10} = 102,000 \text{ tons of coal/month} -$$

$$- 0\cdot00427 \frac{\text{tons of coal}}{\text{m}^3 \text{ of air}} \cdot 17,500,000 \text{ m}^3 \text{ of air/month}$$

$$= 27,275 \text{ tons of coal/month}.$$

The equation of the regression line which gives the average production of coal in relation to the amount of compressed air used, has the following form:

$$\bar{x} = 27,275 \text{ tons of coal/month} + 0\cdot00427 \frac{\text{tons of coal}}{\text{m}^3 \text{ of air}} \cdot y.$$

The regression lines are shown on Graph 1. From the formal statistical point of view both regression lines are of equal importance but in an economic interpretation this is not so. The practical use of the regression line determining the most probable value of production corresponding to a given consumption of one production factor, is rather limited. On the other hand, there is great practical importance in an analysis of the relationship between the volume of production and several production factors. The method of multiple correlation is used for this type of analysis.

The correlation coefficient is a measure of the degree of correlation between the random variables studied. Since it follows from our previous calculations that

$$a_{21} = 156 \frac{\text{m}^3 \text{ of air}}{\text{tons of coal}} , \text{ and } a_{12} = 0\cdot00427 \frac{\text{tons of coal}}{\text{m}^3 \text{ of air}}$$

then on the basis of formula (13)

$$r^2 = 0\cdot00427 \cdot 156 = 0\cdot66612.$$

Hence

$$r = 0\cdot815.$$

The correlation in this case is fairly strong.

Example 2. Analyse the relationship between the average level of inventories and the cost.

A socialist enterprise is an independent economic entity (within the framework of accounting regulations) which tries to fulfil its production targets in the most rational and economical way. This tendency manifests itself in efforts to fulfil and surpass production targets, to observe the production schedules, to improve the quality of the product, to economize and to lower the cost of production. To fulfil these tasks the enterprise is equipped with an appropriate amount of capital goods and liquid assets. It is desirable that the amount of both capital goods and liquid assets necessary to carry out production targets be as low as possible. It is difficult to realize this situation in practice. The amount of capital goods needed is determined by an analysis of the effectiveness of the investments. In the determination of the liquid assets requirements, however, a study of the liquid assets turnover is involved. The purpose of an analysis of the relationship between the average stock of liquid assets and costs is to determine the parameters of the regression equation which enable us to assign an appropriate amount of average stock to particular costs.

The scatter diagram on Graph 2 describes the relationship between the average level of stocks and costs in a clothing factory. The regression line shown on the graph expresses this relationship statistically. On the Y-axis average stocks are measured in millions of zlotys, on the X-axis — costs in millions of zlotys per quarter. The scatter diagram is based on the statistical data shown below, comprising a period of three years. The data come from quarterly accounting reports. The statistical material and the computations involved in determining the regression parameters are shown in Table 2.

Table 2

Average Level of Stocks and Costs in a Clothing Factory

No	x	y	$x-\bar{x}$ +	$x-\bar{x}$ −	$y-\bar{y}$ +	$y-\bar{y}$ −	$(x-\bar{x})^2$	$(x-\bar{x})(y-\bar{y})$ +	$(x-\bar{x})(y-\bar{y})$ −
1	8·3	12·6		5·4		1·8	29·16	9·72	
2	10·2	12·1		3·5		2·3	12·25	8·05	
3	11·5	12·9		2·2		1·5	4·84	3·30	
4	12·2	13·8		1·5		0·6	2·25	0·90	
5	12·4	13·1		1·3		1·3	1·69	1·69	
6	13·7	14·8	0	0	0·4		0	0	
7	14·6	14·7	0·9		0·3		0·81	0·27	
8	14·9	15·3	1·2		0·9		1·44	1·08	
9	16·0	15·7	2·3		1·3		5·29	2·99	
10	16·5	16·0	2·8		1·6		7·84	4·48	
11	16·6	15·5	2·9		1·1		8·41	3·19	
12	17·5	16·3	3·8		1·9		14·44	7·22	
Σ	164·4	172·8	13·9	13·9	7·5	7·5	88·42	42·89	

$\bar{x} = 13\cdot7$, $\bar{y} = 14\cdot4$.

Let us calculate the parameters of the regression line of Y on X:

$$a_{21} = \frac{42\cdot89}{88\cdot42} = 0\cdot476, \quad b_{20} = 14\cdot4 - 0\cdot476 \cdot 13\cdot7 = 7\cdot9.$$

The regression equation that we are trying to find has the following form:

$$y = 7\cdot9 \text{ million zlotys} + 0\cdot476 \text{ quarters} \cdot x.$$

In this example we are not trying to determine the regression line of X on Y or the correlation coefficient.

The regression line is a good tool for appraising the average level of stocks; if the points corresponding to new reporting data appear above the regression line, this means — assuming that the points belong to the same population on which the regression line is based — that there was a set-back in the efforts to increase the turnover of liquid assets; and vice versa, if the points are below the line it indicates that the turnover of liquid assets has risen.

GRAPH 2.

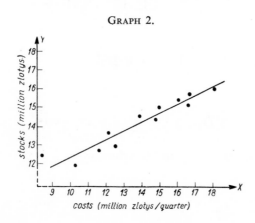

Correlation analysis can be applied to other problems related to the analysis of liquid assets. By studying the relationship between the volume of production in a given period of time and the average level of warehouse stocks we could determine whether such a relationship exists and what its degree is. This would provide valuable material for setting stock control norms and appraising the efficiency of the merchandise control department. Another yardstick for measuring its efficiency is provided by a study of the relationship between the flow of incoming and outgoing warehouse stocks measured in predetermined periods of time.

8

3.2.2. The technique of computing regression parameters in a small and a large sample[1]. Contingency table

*   The computation process connected with the determination of regression parameters in a small sample can be simplified by replacing the differences $(x_i - \bar{x})$ and $(y_i - \bar{y})$ by $(x_i - u)$ and $(y_i - w)$ where u and w are certain constants selected so as to facilitate computation.

Let us denote

$$\bar{x} = u + \Delta_u, \ \ \bar{y} = w + \Delta_w.$$

Since

$$\sum_{i=1}^{n} (x_i - u)^2 = \sum_{i=1}^{n} [x_i - (\bar{x} - \Delta_u)]^2 = \sum_{i=1}^{n} (x_i - \bar{x})^2 + n\Delta_u^2,$$

then

$$\sum_{i=1}^{n} (x_i - \bar{x})^2 = \sum_{i=1}^{n} (x_i - u)^2 - n\Delta_u^2. \tag{1}$$

In consequence of similar transformations it is easy to show that

$$\sum_{i=1}^{n} (y_i - \bar{y})^2 = \sum_{i=1}^{n} (y_i - w)^2 - n\Delta_w^2 \tag{2}$$

and

$$\sum_{i=1}^{n} (x_i - \bar{x})(y_i - \bar{y}) = \sum_{i=1}^{n} (x_i - u)(y_i - w) - n\Delta_u\Delta_w. \tag{3}$$

Therefore

$$a_{21} = \frac{\sum_{i=1}^{n} (x_i - u)(y_i - w) - n\Delta_u\Delta_w}{\sum_{i=1}^{n} (x_i - u)^2 - n\Delta_u^2}, \tag{4}$$

---

[1] Samples comprising not more than 30 items we shall call *small*. Other samples we shall call *large*.

$$a_{12} = \frac{\sum\limits_{i=1}^{n} (x_i - u)(y_i - w) - n\,\Delta_u\Delta_w}{\sum\limits_{i=1}^{n} (y_i - w)^2 - n\,\Delta_w^2}. \tag{5}$$

When the sample is large the *contingency table* is often used for computing regression parameters (Table 1). The top row of the table contains the centres of class intervals of the distribution of y's and in the left column the centres of class intervals of the distribution of x's are shown. The bottom row contains the frequencies $n_{.1}$, $n_{.2}$, ..., $n_{.l}$ of the distribution of y's and the extreme right-hand column — the frequencies $n_{1.}$, $n_{2.}$, ..., $n_{k.}$ of the distribution of x's.

TABLE 1
CONTINGENCY TABLE

X \ Y	y_1	y_2	$\cdots$	y_j	$\cdots$	y_l	
x_1	n_{11}	n_{12}	$\cdots$	n_{1j}	$\cdots$	n_{1l}	$n_{1.}$
x_2	n_{21}	n_{22}		n_{2j}	$\cdots$	n_{2l}	$n_{2.}$
.	.	.	.	.	.	.	.
x_i	n_{i1}	n_{i2}	$\cdots$	n_{ij}	$\cdots$	$n_{i l}$	$n_{i.}$
.	.	.	.	.	.	.	.
x_k	n_{k1}	n_{k2}	$\cdots$	n_{kj}	$\cdots$	n_{kl}	$n_{k.}$
	$n_{.1}$	$n_{.2}$	$\cdots$	$n_{.j}$	$\cdots$	$n_{.l}$	n

In the contingency table the frequency distribution in the sample is shown. The number n in the extreme lower right-hand panel denotes the size of the sample.

Let us write down three important relationships following directly from the contingency table:

$$n_{i.} = \sum_j n_{ij}, \tag{6}$$

$$n_{\cdot j} = \sum_i n_{ij}, \qquad (7)$$

$$n = \sum_i n_{i\cdot} = \sum_j n_{\cdot j} = \sum_i \sum_j n_{ij}. \qquad (8)$$

Assuming that the values of the random variable X and of the random variable Y which belong to particular classes of the frequency distribution are equal to the central values of these classes we get

$$\bar{x} = \frac{1}{n} \sum_i n_{i\cdot} x_i, \qquad (9)$$

$$\bar{y} = \frac{1}{n} \sum_j n_{\cdot j} y_j, \qquad (10)$$

$$a_{21} = \frac{\sum_i \sum_j n_{ij}(x_i - \bar{x})(y_j - \bar{y})}{\sum_i n_{i\cdot}(x_i - \bar{x})^2}; \qquad (11)$$

$$a_{12} = \frac{\sum_i \sum_j n_{ij}(x_i - \bar{x})(y_j - \bar{y})}{\sum_j n_{\cdot j}(y_j - \bar{y})^2}, \qquad (12)$$

$$b_{20} = \bar{y} - a_{21}\bar{x}, \qquad (13)$$

$$b_{10} = \bar{x} - a_{12}\bar{y}. \qquad (14)$$

Computations connected with the application of formulae (11) and (12) may be simplified when the ranges of all the intervals for each variable are the same. Instead of x and y we then introduce the new variables

$$u = \frac{x - u'}{d}, \qquad (15)$$

$$w = \frac{y - w'}{h}, \qquad (16)$$

where u' and w' are constants, d is the range of the class interval for the distribution of x's and h is the range of the class interval for the distribution of y's. We have:

$$x - \bar{x} = u' + ud - u' - \bar{u}d = d(u - \bar{u}), \qquad (17)$$

and similarly

$$y - \bar{y} = h(w - \bar{w}). \qquad (18)$$

Introducing (17) and (18) in (11) and (12) we get

$$a_{21} = \frac{h \sum_i \sum_j n_{ij}(u_i - \bar{u})(w_j - \bar{w})}{d \sum_i n_{i.}(u_i - \bar{u})^2}, \qquad (19)$$

$$a_{12} = \frac{d \sum_i \sum_j n_{ij}(u_i - \bar{u})(w_j - \bar{w})}{h \sum_j n_{.j}(w_j - \bar{w})}. \qquad (20)$$

Now we have to take only one step to arrive at the formulae which are needed to compute parameters a_{21} and a_{12} on the basis of the data in the contingency table. After simple transformations we have

$$a_{21} = \frac{h \left(\dfrac{1}{n} \sum_i \sum_j n_{ij} u_i w_j - \bar{u}\bar{w} \right)}{d(\overline{u^2} - \bar{u}^2)} = \frac{h(\overline{uw} - \bar{u}\bar{w})}{d(\overline{u^2} - \bar{u}^2)}, \qquad (21)$$

$$a_{12} = \frac{d \left(\dfrac{1}{n} \sum_i \sum_j n_{ij} u_i w_j - \bar{u}\bar{w} \right)}{h(\overline{w^2} - \bar{w}^2)} = \frac{d(\overline{uw} - \bar{u}\bar{w})}{h(\overline{w^2} - \bar{w}^2)}. \qquad (22)$$

We shall illustrate the technique of calculating regression parameters by two examples. The first will show the calculation of regression parameters from a small sample and the second -- from a large sample.

Example 1. An analysis and comparison of welfare in different countries is important and interesting, although difficult. The difficulties arise because of differences in national mentalities, traditions, cultures and customs which cause such substantial differences in the average structure of wants in different countries that comparisons present a multitude of problems. The different price and wage ratios in the various countries studied and the necessity of rate of exchange computations magnify these difficulties. However, it is relatively easy to achieve at least some of the research objectives with the help of correlation analysis. The higher the level of welfare in the country the greater number of wants is included in the basic wants group (see 2.2.1.). The characteristic distinguishing basic wants from others is the fact that the relationship between the degree of satisfaction of these wants and income is rather weak. Food constitutes the most important group of basic wants. In our further considerations we shall assume that the consumer in the country studied is able to find on the market every food product he demands. This assumption means that in all countries studied, the buying inducements to which the consumer is exposed with regard to food products are the same. Let us also assume that people in all countries — if they had sufficient financial means at their disposal — would satisfy their nutrition requirements in such a way as to maximize their satisfaction. On the basis of these assumptions we can say that if incomes were sufficiently high people would satisfy their food requirements in the best possible way, earmarking a sufficiently large portion of their income for this purpose. Since food requirements have been made optimum then the portion of income earmarked for food will not increase with a further increase in income. This means that, other things being equal, the correlation between the expenditures for food and the size of income becomes weaker as income increases.

We can surmise, therefore, that *the correlation coefficient between the level of food expenditures and the size of the consumer's income* is one of the welfare characteristics of a group of people. Of course, there are other yardsticks for measuring welfare.

TABLE 2

MONTHLY INCOME (x) AND EXPENDITURES (y) IN 20 FOUR–MEMBER LOWER SILESIAN FAMILIES

No	x	y	$x-u$ +	$x-u$ −	$y-w$ +	$y-w$ −	$(x-u)^2$	$(y-w)^2$	$(x-u)(y-w)$ +	$(x-u)(y-w)$ −
1	267	141		13	11		169	121		143
2	254	159		26	29		676	841		754
3	249	112		31		18	961	324	558	
4	344	152	64			22	4,096	484	1,408	
5	246	119		34		11	1,156	121	374	
6	411	207	131		77		17,161	5,929	10,087	
7	217	114		63		16	3,969	256	1,008	
8	219	118		61		12	3,721	144	732	
9	359	152	79			22	6,241	484	1,738	
10	378	150	98			20	9,604	400	1,960	
11	256	135		24	5		576	25		120
12	406	160	126			30	15,876	900	3,780	
13	258	117		22		13	484	169	286	
14	213	84		67		46	4,489	2,116	3,082	
15	345	129	65			1	4,225	1		65
16	273	164		7	34		49	1,156		238
17	251	76		29		54	841	2,916	1,566	
18	225	126		55		4	3,025	16	220	
19	254	149		26	19		676	361		494
20	194	113		86		17	7,396	289	1,462	
Σ 5,619		2,677	563	544	269	192	85,391	17,053	28,261	1,814
									26,447	

$\bar{x} = 280{\cdot}95,$ $\bar{y} = 133{\cdot}85,$

$u = 280,$ $\Delta_u = 0{\cdot}95,$

$w = 130,$ $\Delta_w = 3{\cdot}85.$

When the correlation coefficient is close to zero, food requirements are met in an optimum way; when it approaches unity, the satisfaction of food requirements is so poor that the possibility of starvation cannot be excluded. However, when the correlation coefficient is close to zero or unity it ceases to perform its function as a yardstick of welfare. If, for instance, in two countries A and B the correlation coefficient is close to zero we cannot say that the level of welfare is the same in both, but we can say that it is so high that it allows the citizens of both countries to achieve an optimum satisfaction of their food requirements. To compare the level of welfare in the two countries we have to introduce another measure which takes into consideration their unsatisfied needs. Similarly, we cannot contend that the level of welfare is equally low if, in the two countries studied, the coefficient of correlation between food expenditures and income is close to unity. We can say that the standard of living in both countries is low. To decide in which it is lower and in which it is higher we have to obtain additional information.

The correlation coefficient should be used with care in measuring welfare. We should remember that we are measuring a complex phenomenon which depends upon many factors. If we heed this warning the correlation coefficient will be a useful tool for measuring the welfare of a nation.

In accordance with formulae (4) and (5) we have

$$a_{21} = \frac{26,447 - 20 \cdot 0.95 \cdot 3.85}{85,391 - 20 \cdot (0.95)^2} = \frac{26,374}{85,373},$$

$$a_{12} = \frac{26,374}{17,053 - 20 \cdot (3.85)^2} = \frac{26,374}{16,757},$$

$$r^2 = a_{21} \cdot a_{12} = \frac{26,374^2}{85,373 \cdot 16,757},$$

$$r = 0.69.$$

Column x in Table 2 shows the average monthly size of income in tens of zlotys; column y of this table contains the statistical data on average monthly food expenditures, also in tens of zlotys. The statistics pertain to twenty four-member families living in the Lower Silesian area.

With reference to this example let us make the following observation: although the calculation of the correlation coefficient is expedited by the method of least squares, it is a time-consuming operation.

Example 2. One of the most difficult problems that confronts the clothing industry is that of deciding the range of sizes of clothes in order to ensure a good fit for a large number of people. Each size range is characterized by a set of several numbers. The problem consists in assigning these numbers to particular characteristics in such a way as to obtain an appropriate combination. Until 1955 the clothing industry used to solve this problem in a very simple way: a well-proportioned woman and man would be selected as a typical representative of the majority of Poles, and ready-to-wear clothes were made according to their measurements. This method resulted in the production of clothes that could be worn only by a small number of people. Warehouses were overstocked with a large number of unsaleable products. In 1955 anthropologists and mathematicians were called in to help solve the problem. The anthropologists have taken about 85 thousand anthropometric pictures of men, women and children. The results were analysed by mathematicians under the direction of Professor Hugo Steinhaus. The sample was large enough to provide reliable information about the measurements of the whole population. In order to select an appropriate set of characteristics for the model the correlation was calculated for pairs of such characteristics as: height, chest, waist, shoulder, neck, arm measurements. The characteristics selected had a low degree of correlation with one another and strong correlation with other characteristics.

Table 3 is a contingency table containing statistical data and computations connected with the determination of the coefficient of correlation between the chest measurements and the height of 500 men selected at random from all the men included in the anthropometric studies[1].

The above example is a good illustration of how technological and economic problems are interrelated.

The preparation of models is a technological problem but its consequences have an economic aspect. A poorly constructed model results in ill-fitting clothes which nobody wants to wear and consequently in the waste of thousands of metres of expensive material and in thousands of hours wasted by tailors. Without correlation analysis it would be difficult to find proper measurements for the models. This shows how useful and valuable correlation analysis can be for practical purposes if it is skilfully used.

The contingency table contains all the data necessary for the computation of the correlation coefficient. Thus we have:

$$\bar{u} = \frac{8}{500} = 0.016,$$

$$\bar{w} = \frac{87}{500} = 0.174.$$

$$\overline{uv} = \frac{634}{500} = 1.268,$$

$$\overline{u^2} = \frac{1,232}{500} = 2.464,$$

$$\overline{w^2} = \frac{2,497}{500} = 4.994,$$

---

[1] These statistics were obtained through courtesy of Professor Adam Wanke.

w:		-6	-5	-4	-3	-2	-1	0	1	2	3	4	5	6	7	8	$n_{i.}$	$u_i n_{i.}$	$u_i^2 n_{i.}$	$\sum_j n_{ij}w_j$	$u_i\sum_j n_{ij}w_j$
u \ y	x	79	81	83	85	87	89	91	93	95	97	99	101	103	105	107					
-5	152	1		1													2	-10	50	-10	+50
-4	156				1	1			1								3	-12	48	-4	+16
-3	160	1		2	1	3	3	2	1	2	1						16	-48	144	-18	+54
-2	164		2	6	9	15	5	8	9	3	3	1					61	-122	244	-68	+136
-1	168	1		1	3	21	18	21	15	14	7	2	2				105	-105	105	+1	-1
0	172	2		2	9	15	26	28	18	14	9	4					127	0	0	-8	0
1	176			1	6	7	14	23	18	16	9	9		1	1	1	106	106	106	+83	+83
2	180			1		2	11	7	7	7	7	6	1	1			50	100	200	+54	+108
3	184						1	5	4	2	5	3	1	1			22	66	198	+42	+126
4	188					1		2	1	2				1			7	28	112	+13	+52
5	192									1							1	5	25	+2	+10
	$n_{.j}$	5	2	14	29	65	78	96	74	61	41	25	4	4	1	1	500	8	1,232		634
	$w_j n_{.j}$	-30	-10	-56	-87	-130	-78	0	74	122	123	100	20	24	7	8	87				
	$w_j^2 n_{.j}$	180	50	224	261	260	78	0	74	244	369	400	100	144	49	64	2,497				
	$\sum_i n_{ij}u_i$	-9	-4	-21	-22	-49	2	17	8	23	22	26	3	10	1	1	8				
	$w_j\sum_i n_{ij}u_i$	54	20	84	66	98	-2	0	8	46	66	104	15	60	7	8	634				

$$h = 2, \quad d = 4.$$

Hence, on the basis of (21) and (22) we get:

$$a_{21} = \frac{2}{4} \cdot \frac{1 \cdot 268 - 0 \cdot 003}{2 \cdot 464} = \frac{1 \cdot 265}{4 \cdot 928} = 0 \cdot 258,$$

$$a_{12} = \frac{4}{2} \cdot \frac{1 \cdot 265}{4 \cdot 994} = \frac{2 \cdot 530}{4 \cdot 994} = 0 \cdot 506.$$

Therefore

$$r^2 = 0 \cdot 258 \cdot 0 \cdot 506 = 0 \cdot 130548.$$

And finally

$$r = 0 \cdot 361.$$

3.3. *Estimating linear regression parameters by the two-point method*

3.3.1. *The derivation of formulae*

In section 3.1. we gave a brief justification for introducing into regression analysis a new method of estimating regression parameters, which we called the two-point method. It is easy to master and convenient to use. We shall now describe this method.

Let us denote by Ω — as in 3.2.1. — a two-dimensional general population. A pair of values (x, y) of random variable (X, Y) corresponds to each item of this population. *We assume that the regression I lines of the general population are straight lines*, i.e.

$$\hat{y} = \alpha_{21}x + \beta_{20} \tag{1}$$

and

$$\hat{x} = \alpha_{12}x + \beta_{10}, \tag{2}$$

where α_{21}, α_{12}, β_{20} and β_{10} are regression parameters of the general population. We take from this population a random sample ω comprising n items. We get n pairs of numbers (x_i, y_i) $(i = 1, 2, ..., n)$ corresponding to the items drawn. These numbers can be interpreted as the coordinates of points located on a plane. Such a random point corresponds to each item of population Ω.

We compute:

$$\bar{x} = \frac{1}{n} \sum_{i=1}^{n} x_i,$$

$$\bar{y} = \frac{1}{n} \sum_{i=1}^{n} y_i.$$

We divide set ω into two subgroups in such a way that we include in the first subgroup the points *with abscissae X not greater than* $\bar{x}$, and into the second subgroup — all the remaining points. If in the second subgroup there are k points, then in the first there will be $n - k$ points. Let us note that in this division of set ω into two subgroups, quantity k is a random variable which may assume the values $1, 2, ..., n - 1$. Let us denote

$$X_{(1)} = X \mid X \leqslant \bar{x},$$

$$Y_{(1)} = Y \mid X \leqslant \bar{x},$$

$$X_{(2)} = X \mid X > \bar{x}, \tag{3}$$

$$Y_{(2)} = Y \mid X > \bar{x}.$$

We compute

$$\bar{x}_{(1)} = \frac{1}{n-k} \sum x_{(1)}, \qquad \bar{x}_{(2)} = \frac{1}{k} \sum x_{(2)},$$

$$\bar{y}_{(1)} = \frac{1}{n-k} \sum y_{(1)}, \qquad \bar{y}_{(2)} = \frac{1}{k} \sum y_{(2)}.$$

The following theorem can be proved:

THEOREM 1.

$$\begin{vmatrix} \bar{x}_{(1)} & \bar{y}_{<1>} & 1 \\ \bar{x}_{(2)} & \bar{y}_{<2>} & 1 \\ \bar{x} & \bar{y} & 1 \end{vmatrix} = 0. \tag{4}$$

The proof of this theorem is given on p. 213 of the Appendix at the end of the book.

It follows from Theorem 1 that the three points $(\bar{x}_{(1)}, \bar{y}_{<1>})$, $(\bar{x}_{(2)}, \bar{y}_{<2>})$, $(\bar{x}, \bar{y})$ *lie on one straight line. As in the estimate of parameter* α_{21}, *we are proposing to accept the slope of this line*; it can be expressed by any one of the following three formulae:

$$a_{21} = \frac{y_{<2>} - \bar{y}}{\bar{x}_{(2)} - \bar{x}}, \tag{5}$$

$$a_{21} = \frac{\bar{y} - \bar{y}_{<1>}}{\bar{x} - \bar{x}_{(1)}}, \tag{6}$$

$$a_{21} = \frac{\bar{y}_{<2>} - \bar{y}_{<1>}}{\bar{x}_{(2)} - \bar{x}_{(1)}}. \tag{7}$$

An estimate of parameter β_{20} can also be expressed in one of the following three ways:

$$b_{2)} = \bar{y}_{<2>} - a_{21}\bar{x}_{(2)}, \tag{8}$$

$$b_{20} = \bar{y}_{<1>} - a_{21}\bar{x}_{(1)}, \tag{9}$$

$$b_{20} = \bar{y} - a_{21}\bar{x}. \tag{10}$$

In order to obtain analogous formulae for estimates of parameters α_{12} and β_{10} we have to divide the set of points ω into two subgroups in such a way that in the first subgroup are points with *ordinates Y not greater than* $\bar{y}$, and in the second, all remaining points.

Let us further denote:

$$Y_{(1)} = Y \mid Y \leqslant \bar{y},$$
$$X_{\langle 1 \rangle} = X \mid Y \leqslant \bar{y},$$
$$Y_{(2)} = Y \mid Y > \bar{y},$$
$$X_{\langle 2 \rangle} = X \mid Y > \bar{y}.$$

(11)

Below are the definitions of other symbols:

$$\bar{y}_{(1)} = \frac{1}{n-m} \sum y_{(1)}, \quad \bar{y}_{(2)} = \frac{1}{m} \sum y_{(2)},$$

$$\bar{x}_{\langle 1 \rangle} = \frac{1}{n-m} \sum x_{\langle 1 \rangle}, \quad \bar{x}_{\langle 2 \rangle} = \frac{1}{m} \sum x_{\langle 2 \rangle}.$$

Letter m stands for the number of points which are in the second subgroup as a result of the division of the ω into two subgroups. Of course, m is a random variable which may assume the values $1, 2, ..., n-1$. By interchanging letters in formulae (5—10) we get the formulae for the regression parameters of X on Y.

$$a_{12} = \frac{\bar{x}_{\langle 2 \rangle} - \bar{x}}{\bar{y}_{(2)} - \bar{y}}, \tag{12}$$

$$a_{12} = \frac{\bar{x} - \bar{x}_{\langle 1 \rangle}}{\bar{y} - \bar{y}_{(1)}}, \tag{13}$$

$$a_{12} = \frac{\bar{x}_{\langle 2 \rangle} - \bar{x}_{\langle 1 \rangle}}{\bar{y}_{(2)} - \bar{y}_{(1)}}. \tag{14}$$

$$b_{10} = \bar{x}_{\langle 2 \rangle} - a_{12}\bar{y}_{(2)}, \tag{15}$$

$$b_{10} = \bar{x}_{\langle 1 \rangle} - a_{12}\bar{y}_{(1)}, \tag{16}$$

$$b_{10} = \bar{x} - a_{12}\bar{y}. \tag{17}$$

It follows from the definition of these regression parameters that all that is required to determine the position of the regression line by the two-point method is to know how to draw a straight line through two points. *When we want to determine the position of the regression line of Y on X we draw a line through any two of the three points* $(\bar{x}_{(1)}, \bar{y}_{<1>})$, $(\bar{x}_{(2)}, \bar{y}_{<2>})$, $(\bar{x}, \bar{y})$. *Similarly when we want to determine the position of the regression line of X on Y we draw a line through any two of the three points* $(\bar{y}_{(1)}, \bar{x}_{<1>})$, $(\bar{y}_{(2)}, \bar{x}_{<2>})$, $(\bar{y}, \bar{x})$.

3.3.2. *The technique of computing regression parameters in a small and a large sample. Examples*

It is easy to use the formulae given in 3.3.1. We shall illustrate this by two examples. In the first example the statistical material covers a period of two years. The regression parameters have been calculated by two methods: by the method of least squares and by the two-point method. This will enable us to show the advantages of using the two-point method. Comparing the computation tables for the two methods we can see that the two-point method is simpler than the classical, easier to comprehend and to compute. In Example 2 illustrating the determination of regression parameters by the two-point method in *a large sample*, we shall not calculate these parameters by the method of least squares. However, to make possible in Example 2 a comparison of the two methods and of the results obtained by them we shall use the statistical data of Example 2 from 3.2.2.

Example 1. Table 1 contains data on the number of car-kilometres driven and the number of kWh used up by the cars of the City Transport Corporation in Wrocław (monthly data).

TABLE 1

KILOMETRES DRIVEN AND kWH USED BY ELECTRIC CARS IN WROCŁAW

No	x car-km	y kWh	No	x car-km	y kWh
1	1,162,697	885,999	13	1,327,516	1,055,148
2	1,033,608	803,399	14	1,221,159	961,312
3	1,093,926	819,134	15	1,372,107	1,091,060
4	1,080,507	788,863	16	1,302,451	1,056,694
5	1,209,917	857,770	17	1,401,363	1,092,946
6	1,128,658	867,890	18	1,495,300	1,094,767
7	1,201,090	917,318	19	1,498,257	1,060,927
8	1,215,048	953,802	20	1,503,663	1,046,036
9	1,190,704	955,560	21	1,479,019	1,258,528
10	1,242,228	996,482	22	1,575,782	1,133,920
11	1,212,823	865,628	23	1,597,701	1,184,790
12	1,252,190	882,888	24	1,617,143	1,237,667

We want to calculate the regression parameters by the method of least squares and by the two-point method: we shall start by rounding off the figures to the nearest ten thousand car-kilometres and ten thousand kWh.

Below is shown the sequence of computing regression parameters by the method of least squares:

9

TABLE 2

METHOD OF LEAST SQUARES APPLIED TO TABLE 1

No	x 10thous. car-km	y 10thous. kWh	$x-u$ +	$x-u$ −	$y-w$ +	$y-w$ −	$(x-u)^2$	$(y-w)^2$	$(x-u)(y-w)$ +	$(x-u)(y-w)$ −
1	116	89		14		11	196	121	154	
2	103	80		27		20	729	400	540	
3	109	82		21		18	441	324	378	
4	108	78		22		21	484	441	462	
5	121	86		9		14	81	196	126	
6	113	87		17		13	289	169	221	
7	120	92		10		8	100	64	80	
8	121	95		9		5	81	25	45	
9	119	96		11		4	121	16	44	
10	124	100		6	0	0	36	0	0	
11	121	87		9		13	81	169	117	
12	125	83		5		12	25	144	60	
13	133	106	3		6		9	36	18	
14	122	96		8		4	64	16	32	
15	137	109	7		9		49	81	63	
16	130	106	0	0	6		0	36	0	
17	140	109	10		9		100	81	90	
18	150	109	20		9		400	81	180	
19	150	106	20		6		400	36	120	
20	150	105	20		5		400	25	100	
21	148	126	18		26		324	676	468	
22	158	113	28		13		784	169	364	
23	160	118	30		18		900	324	540	
24	162	124	32		24		1,024	576	768	
Σ	3,140	2,387	188	168	131	143	7,118	4,206	4,970	

$\bar{x} = 131, \quad \bar{y} = 99 \cdot 5,$

$u = 130, \quad w = 100,$

$$a_{21} = 0 \cdot 699, \qquad a_{12} = 1 \cdot 180,$$

$$r^2 = 0 \cdot 699 \cdot 1 \cdot 180 = 0 \cdot 83,$$

$$r = 0 \cdot 91.$$

In the following table the computation of regression parameters by two-point method is shown:

TABLE 3
TWO-POINT METHOD APPLIED TO TABLE 1

No	x	y	$x_{(2}$	$y_{\langle 2 \rangle}$	$y_{(2)}$	$x_{\langle 2 \rangle}$
1	116	89				
2	103	80				
3	109	82				
4	108	78				
5	121	86				
6	113	87				
7	120	92				
8	121	95				
9	119	96				
10	124	100v			100	124
11	121	87				
12	125	88				
13	133*	106v	133	106	106	133
14	122	96				
15	137*	109v	137	109	109	137
16	130	106v			106	130
17	140*	109v	140	109	109	140
18	150*	109v	150	109	109	150
19	150*	106v	150	106	106	150
20	150*	105v	150	105	105	150
21	148*	126v	148	126	126	148
22	158*	113v	158	113	113	158
23	160*	118v	160	118	118	160
24	162*	124v	162	124	124	162
Σ	3,140	2,387	1,488	1,125	1,331	1,742

$\overline{x} = 130 \cdot 8, \quad \overline{y} = 99 \cdot 5, \quad \overline{x}_{(2)} = 148 \cdot 8, \quad \overline{y}_{\langle 2 \rangle} = 112 \cdot 5, \quad \overline{y}_{(2)} = 110 \cdot 9, \quad \overline{x}_{\langle 2 \rangle} = 145 \cdot 2,$

$$a_{21} = 0 \cdot 72, \qquad a_{12} = 1 \cdot 26,$$

$$r^2 = 0 \cdot 72 \cdot 1 \cdot 26 = 0 \cdot 91,$$

$$r = 0 \cdot 95.$$

ҁ*

Comparing Tables 2 and 3 we can easily see that the computations connected with the determination of regression parameters by the two-point method are much simpler and less time-consuming than those required for the method of least squares.

Let us explain the sequence of computations that have been made in order to fill in Table 3 and to find the values of regression parameters:

1) the figures in columns x and y have been added and the arithmetic means calculated

$$x = \frac{3,140}{24} = 131, \qquad \bar{y} = \frac{2,387}{24} = 99{\cdot}5;$$

2) in column x the numbers greater than $\bar{x} = 131$ have been marked with a *; there are ten of them;

3) the marked values of column x have been written down in column $x_{(2)}$, and the corresponding values of y in column $y_{(2)}$;

4) in column y the numbers greater then $\bar{y} = 99{\cdot}5$ have been marked with a ^{V}; there are twelve of them;

5) the marked values of y have been written down in column $y_{(2)}$, and the corresponding values of x in column $x_{(2)}$;

6) the following averages have been calculated:

$$\bar{x}_{(2)} = \frac{1,488}{10} = 148{\cdot}8, \qquad \bar{y}_{(2)} = \frac{1,125}{10} = 112{\cdot}5,$$

$$\bar{y}_{(2)} = \frac{1,331}{12} = 110{\cdot}9, \qquad \bar{x}_{(2)} = \frac{1,742}{12} = 145{\cdot}2;$$

7) using formulae (5) and (12), a_{21} and a_{12} have been calculated:

$$a_{21} = \frac{112{\cdot}5 - 99{\cdot}5}{148{\cdot}8 - 130{\cdot}8} = 0{\cdot}722,$$

$$a_{12} = \frac{145{\cdot}2 - 130{\cdot}8}{110{\cdot}9 - 99{\cdot}5} = 1{\cdot}263.$$

Knowing the estimates of the regression parameters we can estimate the value of the correlation coefficient. We have:

$$r^2 = a_{21} \cdot a_{12} = 0 \cdot 722 \cdot 1 \cdot 263 = 0 \cdot 9119.$$

Hence:

$$r = 0 \cdot 95.$$

To fill in the computation table in the two-point method *does not require any calculations*. We simply write down in the appropriate columns the numbers marked * and ᵛ, and their corresponding "joint"[1] numbers.

It is not necessary to subtract, square and multiply the numbers with different signs as was the case when the method of least squares was used. If the assumption about the *linear* character of correlation between variables X and Y is valid, both methods give approximately the same results, as can be seen from our example:

GRAPH 1.

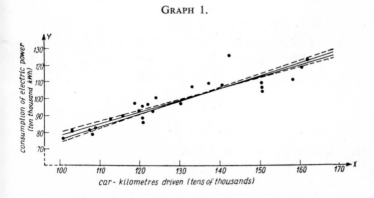

---

[1] The word "joint" is used here in the following sense: since we deal with a two-dimensional random variable for every abscissa x_i there is a joint ordinate y_i, and vice versa, for every ordinate y_i there is a joint abscissa x_i.

On Graph 1 are shown two regression lines determined by the method of least squares (broken lines), and two regression lines determined by the two-point method (continuous lines). There is very little difference in the location of the lines obtained by the two methods, although the dispersion of points is considerable.

* **Example 2.** On the basis of the data contained in Table 3 of 3.2.2., calculate by the two-point method the value both of the regression parameters and of the correlation coefficient.

The solution of this problem is facilitated by Table 4. In addition to the symbols already denoted and defined there are some new ones:

$n_{\langle 1 \cdot \rangle}$, the frequency of variable $X_{\langle 1 \rangle}$,

$n_{\langle 2 \cdot \rangle}$,, ,, ,, ,, $X_{\langle 2 \rangle}$

$n_{\langle \cdot 1 \rangle}$,, ,, ,, ,, $Y_{\langle 1 \rangle}$

$n_{\langle \cdot 2 \rangle}$,, ,, ,, ,, $Y_{\langle 2 \rangle}$

It follows from the general form of Theorem 1, 3.3.1. (see note on p. 214) that set ω can be divided into two subgroups not only by using numbers $\bar{x}$ and $\bar{y}$, but also by using any numbers x_1 and y_1 that satisfy the inequalities

$$x_{\min} \leqslant x_1 \leqslant x_{\max}$$

$$y_{\min} \leqslant y_1 \leqslant y_{\max}.$$

It was assumed in Table 4 that

$$x_1 = 172, \quad y_1 = 91.$$

The division of set ω into subgroups was marked in the table by two thick lines perpendicular to one another and intersecting the middle part of the table cross-wise.

Let us compute the arithmetic means appearing in the formulae for the regression coefficients. All the information

This page is occupied by a single large bivariate correlation / regression worksheet, printed sideways. The table is reproduced below. The body of the table gives the cell frequencies of y (rows, with coded value u) against x (columns, with coded value w); the surrounding rows and columns give the marginal sums used in estimating the regression parameters. Interior cell placements are a best reading of a very dense, rotated worksheet.

y	u	n_{i1}	$u_i n_{\langle i_1\rangle}$	x=79	81	83	85	87	89	91	93	95	97	99	101	103	105	107	$n_{\langle i_2\rangle}$	$u_i n_{\langle i_2\rangle}$	$n_{i\cdot}$	$n_{i\cdot}u_i$
				w=−6	−5	−4	−3	−2	−1	0	1	2	3	4	5	6	7	8				
152	−5	2	−10	1		1															2	−10
156	−4	2	−8				1	1	3										1	−4	3	−12
160	−3	12	−36	1	2	2	1	3	5	2									4	−12	16	−48
164	−2	45	−90			6	9	15	18	8									16	−32	61	−122
168	−1	65	−65	1		1	3	21	26	21	1								40	−40	105	−105
172	0	82	0	2		2	9	15	14	28	9	2							45	0	127	0
176	1	51	51			1	6	7	11	23	18	3	1						55	55	106	106
180	2	21	42			1		2	1	7	18	15	3	1					29	58	50	100
184	3	6	18					1	1	5	15	16	7	2	2				16	48	22	66
188	4	3	12							2	7	8	9	4	1	1			4	16	7	28
192	5										4	4	9	9		2	1	1	1	5	1	5
$n_{\langle\cdot1\rangle}$		289	−86	5	2	12	23	55	52	59	44	32	20	7	2	1	1		211/186	74	314	−297 / 305
$w_j n_{\langle\cdot1\rangle}$				−30	−10	−48	−69	−110	−52	0	44	64	60	28	10	6	7	8				−107
$n_{\langle\cdot2\rangle}$						2	6	10	26	37	30	29	21	18	2	3		1	193			
$n_{\cdot j}$				5	2	14	29	65	78	96	74	61	41	25	4	4	1	1	211			
$n\cdot_j w_j$				−30	−10	−56	−87	−130	−78	0	74	122	123	100	20	24	7	8	478			−391

needed for calculating these averages is provided by Table 4. Thus we have:

$$\bar{x}_{(1)} = 172 - \frac{297}{314} \cdot 4 = 168 \cdot 22,$$

$$\bar{x}_{(2)} = 172 + \frac{305}{186} \cdot 4 = 178 \cdot 52,$$

$$\bar{y}_{(1)} = 91 - \frac{391}{289} \cdot 2 = 88 \cdot 30,$$

$$\bar{y}_{(2)} = 91 + \frac{478}{211} \cdot 2 = 95 \cdot 52,$$

$$\bar{y}_{\langle 1 \rangle} = 91 - \frac{107}{314} \cdot 2 = 90 \cdot 32,$$

$$\bar{y}_{\langle 2 \rangle} = 91 + \frac{193}{186} \cdot 2 = 93 \cdot 08,$$

$$\bar{x}_{\langle 1 \rangle} = 172 - \frac{86}{289} \cdot 4 = 170 \cdot 81,$$

$$\bar{x}_{\langle 2 \rangle} = 172 + \frac{74}{211} \cdot 4 = 173 \cdot 40,$$

Hence

$$a_{21} = \frac{93 \cdot 08 - 90 \cdot 32}{178 \cdot 52 - 168 \cdot 22} = 0 \cdot 267,$$

$$a_{12} = \frac{173 \cdot 40 - 170 \cdot 81}{95 \cdot 52 - 88 \cdot 30} = 0 \cdot 359,$$

$$r^2 = 0 \cdot 0958,$$

$$r = 0 \cdot 309.$$

**

On Graph 2 two pairs of regression lines are shown. The broken lines are the regression lines determined by the method of least squares (see 3.2.2., Example 2) and the continuous lines are the regression lines determined by the two-point method.

GRAPH 2.

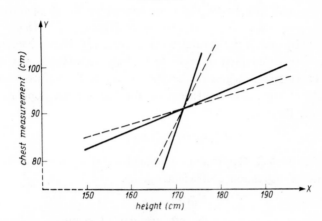

As can be seen from the graph, the positions of the lines determined by the two methods are not very different, in spite of the fact that the correlation is fairly weak (i.e. the points are widely scattered on the scatter diagram).

3.3.3. *The properties of estimates obtained by the two-point method*

In both examples discussed above we have seen that the numerical results of estimating regression parameters by the method of least squares and the two-point method did not differ much. The computations in both cases were based on the actual statistical material so that there is no question of selecting the figures on purpose in such a way as to obtain similar results. The similarity can be explained by certain general properties of estimates obtained by both methods. As we know (see 3.1.), the estimates of regression parameters obtained by the classical method *are consistent and unbiased. Estimates obtained by the two-point method have similar properties.* This explains the similarity of the results noticeable in Examples 1 and 2 of 3.3.2.

We shall give below theorems concerning the most important properties of the regression coefficient a_{21} defined in 3.3.1. by one of the formulae (5), (6) and (7). These theorems can also be adapted to apply to the regression coefficient a_{12}.

THEOREM 1. Regression coefficient a_{21} is a consistent estimate of regression coefficient a_{21} for the general population Ω, i.e. for every $\varepsilon > 0$

$$P\{|a_{21} - a_{21}| > \varepsilon\} \underset{n \to \infty}{\to} 0. \tag{1}$$

THEOREM 2. Regression coefficient a_{21} is an unbiased estimate of regression coefficient a_{21}, i.e.

$$E(a_{21}) = a_{21}. \tag{2}$$

In order to appraise the effectiveness of estimates obtained by the two-point method we should compare the variance of these estimates with the variance of the estimates obtained by the method of least squares. We know from the Markoff Theorem that the estimates obtained by the classical method have a minimum variance. To distinguish between estimates obtained by the two methods we shall denote them as follows:

$a_{21\text{class}}$ — the regression coefficient obtained by the method of least squares,

$a_{21\text{point}}$ — the regression coefficient obtained by the two-point method.

Let us also denote:

$$V(a_{21\ \text{class}}) = V(a_{21\ \text{class}} \mid x_1 = u_1, ..., x_n = u_n),$$

$$V(a_{21\ \text{point}}) = V(a_{21\ \text{point}} \mid x_1 = u_1, ..., x_n = u_n),$$

$$s_u = \sqrt{\frac{1}{n} \sum (u - \overline{u})^2}, \quad d_u = \frac{1}{n} \sum |u - \overline{u}|,$$

where $u_1, u_2, ..., u_n$ are certain constants.

THEOREM 3.

$$e(a_{21 \text{ point}} \mid x_1 = u_1, \ldots, x_n = u_n)$$

$$= \frac{V(a_{21 \text{ class}})}{V(a_{21 \text{ point}})} \geqslant \frac{d_u^2}{s_u^2} \cdot \frac{n-1}{n}. \tag{3}$$

Applying the Slutsky Theorem to the right side of formula (3), we find that e converges in probability to D_x^2/σ_x^2 where

$$D_x = \int\limits_{-\infty}^{\infty} |x - m_1| f_1(x) dx, \quad \sigma_x^2 = \int\limits_{-\infty}^{\infty} (x - m_1)^2 f_1(x) \, dx.$$

The definition of symbol $f_1(x)$ is given in 1.2.3., formula (6). If the distribution of population Ω is normal (see 1.2.9., formula (1)), then e converges in probability to $2/\pi$. It is interesting to note that if the random variable X has a normal distribution $N(m, \sigma)$ then the effectiveness of the median as an estimate of parameter m is also equal to $2/\pi$.

THEOREM 4. The distribution of random variable

$$\frac{a_{21} - \alpha_{21}}{\sqrt{V(a_{21})}} \tag{4}$$

approaches a normal distribution $N(0, 1)$ for $n \to \infty$. The proofs of Theorems 1–4 are given in [31].

3.3.4. Comments on estimating the correlation coefficient by the two-point method

In examples 1 and 2 we have estimated correlation coefficient ϱ in population Ω by the formula

$$r^2 = a_{21} \cdot a_{12},$$

where a_{21} and a_{12} are regression coefficients obtained by the two-point method. This procedure is justified by the Slutsky Theorem which states that if random variables $X_n, Y_n, \ldots, Z_n$ are stochastically convergent to the constants $x, y, \ldots, z$, then any rational function of these variables $R(X_n, \ldots, Z_n)$ is stochastically convergent to the constant $R(x, y, \ldots, z)$.

To prove that

$$r = \sqrt{a_{21} \cdot a_{12}}$$

tends in probability to correlation coefficient ϱ we shall prove the following theorem.

THEOREM 1. Let the sequence $\{X_n\}$ of random variables tend with probability 1 to the number a, and let $\psi(x)$ denote the continuous function of x. Then the sequence $\{\psi(X_n)\}$ of random variables converges in probability 1 to $\psi(a)$.

Proof.

$$P\left\{\lim_{n\to\infty} X_n = a\right\} = 1.$$

For each continuous function $\psi(x)$, the condition

$$\lim_{n\to\infty} X_n = a$$

means that

$$\lim_{n\to\infty} \psi(X_n) = \psi(a).$$

Hence the events

$$\lim_{n\to\infty} X_n = a \quad \text{and} \quad \lim_{n\to\infty} \psi(X_n) = \psi(a)$$

are equivalent and therefore

$$P\left\{\lim_{n\to\infty} \psi(X_n) = \psi(a)\right\} = 1.$$

It follows from the above theorem that if r^2 converges in probability to ϱ^2, then r tends to ϱ.

In the conclusion of our discussion on estimating the correlation coefficient by the two-point method we should mention one more problem. As we know, the product of the regression coefficients obtained by the method of least squares

$$a_{21\ \text{class}} \cdot a_{12\ \text{class}}$$

is a positive quantity with zero-one norm (see 1.2.8.). The

product of the regression coefficients obtained by the two-point method does not have this property.

We can give numerical examples in which the product

$$a_{21 \text{ point}} \cdot a_{12 \text{ point}}$$

is greater than one or less than zero. If the sample is sufficiently large then, on the assumption that there is linear correlation between the variables studied, the probability of the realization of such an event is negligible because the product $a_{21 \text{ point}} \cdot a_{12 \text{ point}}$ tends stochastically to ϱ^2.

In estimating the correlation coefficient by the two-point method we should observe the following convention:

1) correlation coefficient $r > 0$ when $a_{21} > 0$ and $a_{12} > 0$;
2) correlation coefficient $r < 0$ when $a_{21} < 0$ and $a_{12} < 0$;
3) if $a_{21} \cdot a_{12} > 1$ we assume that $r = 1$;
4) if coefficients a_{21} and a_{12} have different signs we assume that $r = 0$.

When case 3 or 4 occurs in practice we suspect that the assumption about the linearity of correlation is not true. We also suspect this when the product $a_{21} \cdot a_{12} = 1$ but the points on the scatter diagram are *not located* on the straight line (see Graph 3).

GRAPH 3.

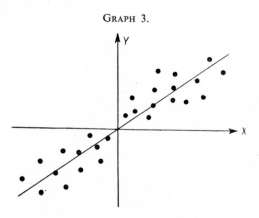

It follows that there are situations in which the two-point method provides reasons for postulating the hypothesis that at least one of the regression lines is not a straight line. This is an important advantage of the two-point method.

4. ON TESTING CERTAIN STATISTICAL HYPOTHESES

4.1. Two tests to verify the hypothesis that the distribution of the general population Ω is normal[1]

4.1.1. The formulation of the problem

In many theorems of theory of probability and mathematical statistics it is assumed that the distribution of the random variable is normal. In practical applications it is often very difficult to check to what extent this assumption is justified. When the subject of statistical research is an ordinary random variable, there are several methods of testing the hypothesis that the distribution of the population is normal. These methods do not provide sufficient grounds for accepting the hypothesis, but in some cases enable us to reject it. The usual procedure in practice is to assume that if the information obtained from the sample does not give grounds for rejecting the hypothesis, it can be regarded as true and can be accepted in the sense that the population is normal, without any further justification. Although this procedure is open to objection it has to be accepted because there is no other sensible way out.

For statistical research involving multi-dimensional random variables, it is more difficult to test the hypothesis that the population is normal. We shall again be concerned here with continuous two-dimensional variables. As we know (e.g. see [7], section 29.6) in many theorems involving such a variable

---

[1] Published in _Przegląd Statystyczny (Statistical Review)_, No. 3, 1957.

it is assumed that its distribution is normal, i.e. that the two-dimensional density function of this distribution is expressed by the formula

$$\varphi(x,y) \tag{1}$$

$$= \frac{1}{2\pi\sigma_1\sigma_2 \sqrt{1-\varrho^2}} \, e^{-\frac{1}{2(1-\varrho^2)}\left[\left(\frac{x-m_1}{\sigma_1}\right)^2 - 2\varrho \frac{x-m_1}{\sigma_1} \cdot \frac{x-m_2}{\sigma_2} + \left(\frac{x-m_2}{\sigma_2}\right)^2\right]}$$

(see 1.2.9., formula (1)).

Let us denote by H the hypothesis that the *two-dimensional random variable (X,Y) has a normal distribution with the density given by* (1).

If follows from the generalization of the Central Limit Theorem on two-dimensional variables (see [7]) that in practice we often deal with this type of distribution. It is difficult to establish this fact by experiment because it is inconvenient to construct spatial diagrams of the distribution. This increases the importance of statistical methods in testing hypothesis H.

The role of these methods is particularly important in selecting a function for the equation of the regression line. As we know (see 1.2.9., Corollary 1) regression I lines are straight lines when the joint distribution of random variable (X,Y) is normal. This explains why we so often deal with linear regression in practice. However, a distribution does not necessarily have to be normal every time a visual inspection of the scatter diagram based on a sample suggests that we deal with linear regression. When a population is normal the regression lines are straight lines, but when the regression lines are straight lines the distribution of the population may or may not be normal. Under these circumstances the results of testing the hypothesis that the distribution is normal may be of great practical importance.

The difficulties encountered in verifying this hypothesis with reference to a two-dimensional random variable are caused by the fact that the tables of the two-dimensional density function for a normal distribution are not easily accessible[1]. In this section we shall discuss two methods of testing the hypothesis that the distribution of a two-dimensional random variable is normal. When these methods are used such tables are not required.

Both methods can be applied to large samples.

4.1.2. Testing hypothesis H by rotating the coordinate system (method A)

The consistency of the two-dimensional distribution of a general population with a normal distribution can be checked by the χ^2 test. As we know (1.2.9., Theorem 1), variables X and Y are stochastically independent when parameter ϱ in a two-dimensional normal distribution equals zero. If parameter $\varrho \neq 0$ we replace random variables X and Y by variables X' and Y' using a linear transformation.

$$X' = (X - m_1) \cos \Theta + (Y - m_1) \sin \Theta,$$
$$Y' = -(X - m_2) \sin \Theta + (Y - m_2) \cos \Theta. \tag{1}$$

Then

$$E(X', Y') = 0, \text{ and hence } \varrho(X', Y') = 0$$

(see 1.2.8., Theorem 4).

Thus we can see that if a joint distribution of a two-dimensional random variable (X', Y') is normal, then these variables are stochastically independent. Hence we can write

$$\varphi(x', y') = \varphi_1(x') \cdot \varphi_2(y'),$$

where $\varphi(x', y')$ denotes the two-dimensional density of the normal distribution of variable (X', Y') and $\varphi_1(x')$ and $\varphi_2(y')$

---

[1] However, such tables exist. See [40], [44].

are the symbols of marginal densities of variables X' and Y' in this distribution. Since a joint distribution is normal, the distributions $\varphi_1(x')$ and $\varphi_2(y')$ are also normal but, of course, in one dimension[1]. The parameters of these distributions are expressed by the formulae:

$$E(X') = E[(X - m_1)\cos\Theta + (Y - m^2)\sin\Theta] = 0,$$

$$E[X' - E(X')]^2 = E[(X - m_1)^2\cos^2\Theta + (Y - m_2)^2\sin^2\Theta +$$
$$+ (X - m_1)(Y - m_2)\sin 2\Theta] = \sigma_1^2\cos^2\Theta + \sigma_2^2\sin^2\Theta,$$

$$E(Y') = E[-(X - m_1)\sin\Theta + (Y - m_2)\cos\Theta] = 0,$$

$$E[Y' - E(Y')]^2 = E[(X - m_1)^2\sin^2\Theta + (Y - m_2)^2\cos^2\Theta -$$
$$- (X - m_1)(Y - m_2)\sin 2\Theta] = \sigma_1^2\sin^2\Theta + \sigma_2^2\cos^2\Theta.$$

The construction of the test for hypothesis H is based on the fact that variables X' and Y' are stochastically independent.

By using the χ^2 test we can easily check whether or not empirical marginal distributions are essentially different from a normal distribution. Let us denote by $v_1(x_i')$ the empirical marginal distribution of variable X' from the sample and by n the size of the sample. In this case the divergence between this empirical distribution of variable X' from the sample and a theoretical normal distribution $\varphi_1(x_i')$ is measured by the expression

$$\chi_x^2 = \sum \frac{[nv_1(x_i') - n\varphi_1(x_i')]^2}{n\varphi_1(x_i')}. \tag{2}$$

For variable Y' we get an analogous expression

$$\chi_y^2 = \sum \frac{[nv_2(y_i') - n\varphi_2(y_i')]^2}{n\varphi_2(y_i')}, \tag{3}$$

where $v_2(y_i')$ denotes the empirical distribution of variable Y'.

---

[1] Tables for a normal distribution in one dimension are given at the end of the book.

We shall denote by α the probability of an event that we consider as practically impossible. There exists a positive real number χ_0^2 dependent upon α and such that

$$P\{\chi_x^2 > \chi_0^2\} = P\{\chi_y^2 > \chi_0^2\} = \alpha.$$

We have further

$$P\{\chi_x^2 \leqslant \chi_0^2\} = 1 - P\{\chi_x^2 > \chi_0^2\}$$

and analogously

$$P\{\chi_y^2 \leqslant \chi_0^2\} = 1 - P\{\chi_y^2 > \chi_0^2\}.$$

It should be remembered that when hypothesis H is true, variables X' and Y' are independent, and so are variables χ_x^2 and χ_y^2.

We reject hypothesis H when

$$(\chi_x^2 > \chi_0^2) \cup (\chi_y^2 > \chi_0^2), \tag{4}$$

where symbol $\cup$ means "or".

The probability of this event is

$$P\{(\chi_x^2 > \chi_0^2) \cup (\chi_y^2 > \chi_0^2)\} = 1 - P\{\chi_x^2 \leqslant \chi_0^2, \chi_y^2 \leqslant \chi_0^2\}$$
$$= 1 - P\{\chi_x^2 \leqslant \chi_0^2\} \cdot P\{\chi_y^2 \leqslant \chi_0^2\} = 1 - (1-\alpha)(1-\alpha)$$
$$= 1 - 1 + 2\alpha - \alpha^2 = 2\alpha - \alpha^2 < 2\alpha.$$

The values of χ_0^2 are taken from appropriate tables[1]. We call the number α the level of significance.

Example 1[2]. In an electric power station the relationship between the consumption of coal and the output of electric power is studied. In Table 1 the statistical material for a 6-year period is shown. The x-column of this table represents the monthly output of electric current (in tens of thousands of kWh) measured at the generator contacts and the y-column

---

[1] χ^2 distribution tables are given at the end of the book.

[2] The statistical data for this example have been obtained through the courtesy of Professor J. Falewicz.

contains the data on the consumption of slack coal (in tens of tons) used for production. The data come from a metalurgical electric power station equipped with two SKODA turbogener-

TABLE 1

CONSUMPTION OF COAL AND ELECTRICITY GENERATED IN AN ELECTRIC POWER STATION

No	x	y	No	x	y	No	x	y	No	x	y
1	183	175	19	190	193	37	180	191	55	180	164
2	184	172	20	180	169	38	170	167	56	207	191
3	180	168	21	169	177	39	182	161	57	190	173
4	164	156	22	206	190	40	189	180	58	185	174
5	177	190	23	199	186	41	213	191	59	186	190
6	159	160	24	201	180	42	301	264	60	181	166
7	147	142	25	207	182	43	225	202	61	192	179
8	151	153	26	209	190	44	234	214	62	203	191
9	164	149	27	184	164	45	203	184	63	277	247
10	122	128	28	165	164	46	192	189	64	299	257
11	167	167	29	142	149	47	191	179	65	215	206
12	188	172	30	116	133	48	146	155	66	200	188
13	180	162	31	147	164	49	193	173	67	192	167
14	156	160	32	175	168	50	187	166	68	187	183
15	163	154	33	197	176	51	187	182	69	194	190
16	175	160	34	202	186	52	212	205	70	194	182
17	173	179	35	189	183	53	251	216	71	190	178
18	158	144	36	190	176	54	220	201	72	278	241

ators, each of 3,100 kW capacity, and two DUQUESNE boilers heated by slack coal. The consumption of slack coal is given in gross terms as recorded during control weighing. The output of power is also given in gross terms because it was measured at the contacts of the generators.

A scatter diagram on the basis of the data given in Table 1 is shown on Graph 1.

GRAPH 1.

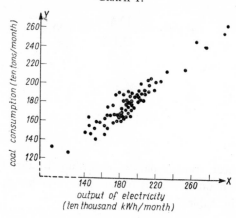

The distribution of the points on the diagram suggests that the distribution of the variable (X, Y) is normal. This hypothesis should be tested. To prepare the statistical material for testing the hypothesis we use formulae for translating and rotating the coordinate system. We find the angle of rotation γ by formula (7) from 1.2.8., replacing the population parameters by the sample parameters. In this way we test the hypothesis that the population has a normal distribution with parameters $m_1 = \bar{x}, m_2 = \bar{y}, \Theta = \gamma$.

Let us denote:

$$\bar{x} = \frac{1}{n} \sum x, \quad \bar{y} = \frac{1}{n} \sum y, \quad n\text{–the size of the sample.}$$

It follows from calculations (see Appendix, pp. 215–216), that

$$\sum (x - \bar{x}) \cdot (y - \bar{y}) = 56,344,$$

$$\sum (x - \bar{x})^2 \qquad = 79,124,$$

$$\sum (y - \bar{y})^2 \qquad = 43,952,$$

Linear regression

therefore

$$\tan 2\gamma = \frac{112{,}688}{35{,}176} = 3{\cdot}20.$$

Further, we have

$$\gamma = 36°21',$$

$$\sin \gamma = 0{\cdot}592,$$

$$\cos \gamma = 0{\cdot}806.$$

After a linear transformation, according to formula (1) in 4.1.2., we obtain the values of the new variables x', y' which are given in Table 2.

TABLE 2

TRANSFORMATION COMPUTATIONS APPLIED TO TABLE 1

№	x'	y'	№	x'	y'	№	x'	y'	№	x'	y'
1	− 8·0	+ 0·9	19	+ 8·3	+11·3	37	− 1·0	+15·6	55	− 16·9	− 6·2
2	− 9·6	− 2·9	20	−14·0	− 2·1	38	−23·2	+ 2·2	56	+ 20·8	− 0·4
3	−14·6	− 3·0	21	+ 3·7	+ 4·2	39	−17·1	− 9·8	57	− 3·6	− 4·8
4	−34·6	− 3·2	22	+19·4	− 1·0	40	− 0·2	+ 1·4	58	− 7·0	− 2·1
5	− 4·0	+16·6	23	+11·4	+ 0·3	41	+25·6	− 4·0	59	− 8·6	− 4·9
6	−36·2	+ 3·0	24	+ 9·5	− 5·8	42	+13·8	+ 2·9	60	− 15·0	− 5·2
7	−56·6	− 4·0	25	+14·5	− 7·6	43	+41·8	− 2·2	61	+ 1·6	− 1·2
8	−46·8	+ 2·1	26	+21·8	− 2·4	44	+56·2	+ 2·2	62	+ 17·6	+ 2·0
9	−38·7	− 8·8	27	−13·6	− 8·5	45	+23·4	− 3·7	63	+110·4	+ 3·3
10	−85·0	− 0·9	28	−29·0	+ 2·7	46	+ 7·5	+ 6·9	64	+134·0	− 1·7
11	−25·6	+ 4·0	29	−56·5	+ 4·2	47	+ 0·8	− 0·6	65	+ 36·1	+ 7·0
12	− 5·8	− 4·7	30	−86·9	+ 6·7	48	−49·7	+ 6·7	66	+ 13·4	+ 1·3
13	−18·1	− 7·8	31	−43·5	+12·4	49	− 1·1	− 6·6	67	− 5·5	−10·9
14	−38·7	+ 4·8	32	−18·6	0·0	50	−10·1	− 8·7	68	− 0·1	+ 5·0
15	−36·6	− 4·2	33	+ 3·9	− 6·6	51	− 0·6	+ 3·2	69	+ 9·7	+ 6·6
16	−23·3	− 5·4	34	+13·8	− 1·5	52	+33·1	+ 7·9	70	+ 4·9	− 0·1
17	−13·7	+10·1	35	+ 1·6	+ 3·8	53	+71·1	− 6·3	71	− 0·6	− 0·8
18	−46·5	− 9·3	36	− 1·8	− 2·4	54	+37·2	0·0	72	+107·6	− 2·1

The scatter diagram for the data in Table 2 is shown below (Graph 2).

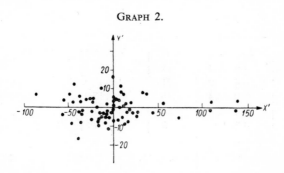

GRAPH 2.

On the basis of the data from Table 2 we now construct a frequency distribution for variable x' and for variable y'. Then on the basis of formulae (2) and (3) we calculate χ_x^2 and χ_y^2 (see Table 3 and Table 4).

TABLE 3

χ^2 TEST APPLIED TO VARIABLE x'

No	x'	n_i	n_i'	$\dfrac{(n_i - n_i')^2}{n_i'}$
1	$-\infty$ -50	$\left.\begin{array}{c}4\\9\end{array}\right\}13$	$\left.\begin{array}{c}8\cdot3\\8\cdot7\end{array}\right\}17$	0·94
2	-50 -30			
3	-30 -10	14	12·1	0·30
4	-10 $+10$	25	13·7	9·32
5	$+10$ $+30$	10	12·1	0·36
6	$+30$ $+\infty$	10	17·1	2·94
		$n = 72$	72·0	13·86

where $n_i = n.v_1(x_i')$, $n_i' = n.\varphi(x_i')$.

TABLE 4

χ^2 TEST APPLIED TO VARIABLE y'

No	y'	n_j	n'_j	$\dfrac{(n_j - n'_j)^2}{n'_j}$
1	$-\infty \quad -8$	$\left.\begin{array}{c}6\\14\end{array}\right\}20$	$\left.\begin{array}{c}7\cdot5\\11\cdot6\end{array}\right\}19\cdot1$	$0\cdot04$
2	$-8 \quad -4$			
3	$-4 \quad 0$	21	$17\cdot0$	$0\cdot94$
4	$0 \quad +4$	16	$17\cdot0$	$0\cdot06$
5	$+4 \quad +8$	$\left.\begin{array}{c}10\\5\end{array}\right\}15$	$\left.\begin{array}{c}11\cdot1\\7\cdot5\end{array}\right\}18\cdot6$	$0\cdot36$
6	$+8 \quad +\infty$			
		$n = 72$	$72\cdot2$	$1\cdot40$

where $n_j = n.v_2(y'_j)$, $\quad n'_j = n.\varphi(y'_j)$.

Let the level of significance $2\alpha = 0\cdot02$. In this case $\alpha = 0\cdot01$. In the χ^2 distribution tables for 4 degrees of freedom we find $\chi_0^2 = 13\cdot277$. Since

$$\chi_x^2 = 13\cdot86 > \chi_0^2 = 13\cdot277$$

we reject hypothesis *H*. We have rejected it on the basis of *the same sample* on which hypothetical parameters of the distribution were determined. Thus the reason for rejecting the hypothesis is that the distribution in *the sample is significantly different from a normal distribution*. If we do not want to stop at comparing the marginal distributions of random variables X' and Y' with a one-dimensional normal distribution by the consistency test, we may check the consistency of the joint distribution of variable (X', Y') with a two-dimensional normal distribution. For this purpose we have to construct a special contingency table and compare the frequencies in particular panels of this table with the theoretical frequencies. The latter are calculated by multiplying the frequencies of the sample by the product of probabilities corresponding to a given panel and taken from marginal distributions. Knowing the frequencies in particular panels of the contingency table and the theoretical frequencies, we can check by the χ^2 test whether these frequencies differ significantly from one another.

The above method of testing hypothesis H requires many cumbersome computations connected with the use of formula (1). We do not refer here to computations connected with the calculation of parameters $\bar{x}$, $\bar{y}$ and the sums:

$$\sum (x - \bar{x})(y - \bar{y}), \quad \sum (x - \bar{x})^2, \quad \sum (y - \bar{y})^2.$$

These computations are needed for all methods of testing hypothesis H. We refer to computations involved in the process of testing the hypothesis. The verification of the hypothesis by the χ^2 test in the way described below requires computations which *become more time-consuming as the size of the sample increases*. This is the drawback of this test. Tests described in textbooks (e.g. see [28][1]) suffer from the same drawback. Only a test for which the time needed for computations does not greatly depend upon the size of the sample, is convenient and practical. This type of test is described below. We shall call it the B test to distinguish it from the test described above which we shall call the A test. The main advantage of the B test is its simplicity: it requires very few computations. The main disadvantage is its low "sensitivity".

4.1.3. *Testing the hypothesis H by dividing the plane into quadrants* (*method B*)

Let us denote by A the event that variable X assumes a value greater than the average value m_1, and variable Y as-

---

[1] A. Hald: *Statistical Theory with Engineering Applications*, New York, 1952, p. 602-604.

sumes a value greater than the average value m_2. This means that

$$A = (X > m_1) \cap (Y > m_2), \tag{1}$$

where $\cap$ means "and".
Let us further denote

$$B = (X \leqslant m_1) \cap (Y \leqslant m_2), \tag{2}$$

$$C = (X > m_1) \cap (Y \leqslant m_2), \tag{3}$$

$$D = (X \leqslant m_1) \cap (Y > m_2). \tag{4}$$

When $m_1 = m_2 = 0$ then A, B, C, D denote events in which point (x, y) lies respectively in the 1st, 3rd, 4th and 2nd quadrant of the coordinate system. It can be shown (see 1.2.9., formula (9)) that

$$p_1 = P(A) = P(B) = \frac{1}{4} + \frac{1}{2\pi} \text{ arc sin } \varrho \tag{5}$$

and

$$p_2 = P(C) = P(D) = \frac{1}{4} - \frac{1}{2\pi} \text{ arc sin } \varrho. \tag{6}$$

Thus we know the probability of the random chance that the point (X, Y) is located in a particular quadrant of the plane. The knowledge of these probabilities allows us to construct a test to verify hypothesis H. This hypothesis may be verified by many tests, but the χ^2 test seems to be the most convenient.

Knowing the probability of a random occurrence of a point in the individual quadrants of the plane, we can easily calculate the hypothetical numbers of points in these quadrants. We shall call these numbers the hypothetical frequencies of the quadrants of the plane. The hypothetical number of points in the individual quadrants will, of course, differ from the empirical number of points. We shall call the empirical number of points the empirical frequency of the quadrant of the plane. Let us denote the hypothetical frequencies by n_i' and the empirical frequencies by n_i ($i = 1$, 2, 3, 4).

The measure of divergence between the hypothetical and empirical frequencies is expressed by the quantity

$$\sum \frac{(n_i' - n_i)^2}{n_i'},$$

which is a random variable and has the χ^2 distribution with three degrees of freedom. We reject hypothesis H when

$$\chi^2 > \chi_0^2,$$

where χ_0^2 is a number dependent upon the significance coefficient α.

The construction of test B is based on the assumption that the population parameters m_1, m_2 and ϱ are known. In practice this happens very rarely. Therefore, when we do not know the values of these parameters we have to substitute for them the estimates from the sample. (A similar procedure was also used in test A.)

Example 1. A sample of 72 items was taken from a two-dimensional population. Each item in the sample may be treated as a point on the plane. The coordinates of these points represent the two-dimensional random variable (X, Y). On the basis of statistical data obtained from the sample we want to check hypothesis H that the distribution of the two-dimensional population is normal. The statistical data are shown in Table 1 in 4.1.2.

It follows from the calculations which we shall not quote here[1] that

---

[1] See the Appendix pp. 215-216.

$$\bar{x} = \frac{1}{n} \sum_1^n x = 190 \cdot 4,$$

$$\bar{y} = \frac{1}{n} \sum_1^n y = 179 \cdot 0,$$

$$r = \frac{\sum\limits_1^n (x-\bar{x})(y-\bar{y})}{\sqrt{\sum\limits_1^n (x-\bar{x})^2 \sum\limits_1^n (y-\bar{y})^2}} = 0 \cdot 96.$$

Assuming that $m_1 = \bar{x}$, $m_2 = \bar{y}$ and $\varrho = r$ we calculate the frequencies of the actual occurences of events A, B, C and D. The occurence of event A is equivalent to a random chance of a point being located in the 1st quadrant of the plane. It is assumed that the origin of the coordinate system lies at point $(\bar{x}, \bar{y})$.

It is easy to check (using Table 1 in 4.1.2.) that event A has occured 24 times, event B 34 times, event C 7 times, event D also 7 times.

Assuming that $\varrho = 0 \cdot 96$ we determine p_1 and p_2 (see formulae (5) and (6)). The values of p_1 and p_2 are functions of ϱ. Different values of parameters p_1 and p_2 correspond to different values of ϱ. They are shown in Table 2. Using this table we find that $p_1 = 0 \cdot 456$ and $p_2 = 0 \cdot 044$ correspond to the number $\varrho = 0 \cdot 96$.

Since we know p_1 and p_2 we can calculate the hypothetical frequencies of points in particular quadrants of the plane and we can check by the χ^2 test the significance of the deviations of the empirical frequencies from the hypothetical frequencies.

The calculations are shown in Table 1.

TABLE 1

χ^2 TEST APPLIED TO VERIFICATION OF HYPOTHESIS H BY DIVIDING THE PLANE INTO QUADRANTS

No (i)	Event	n_i	p_1, p_2	n_i'	$n_i - n_i'$	$(n_i - n_i')^2$	$\dfrac{(n_i - n_i')^2}{n_i'}$
1	A	24	0·456	33·0	−9·0	81·00	2·38
2	B	34	0·456	33·0	1·0	1·00	0·03
3	C	7 ⎱14	0·044	3·2 ⎱6·4	7·6	57·76	9·00
4	D	7 ⎰	0·044	3·2 ⎰			
Total		72	1·000	72·4		$\chi^2 = 11·41$	

Let us assume that the level of significance $\alpha = 0.02$. For this level of significance with two degrees of freedom[1] the corresponding value of χ_0^2 is 7·8. Therefore, hypothesis H should be rejected since

$$\chi^2 = 11·41 > \chi_0^2 = 7·8.$$

We can see from the above example that test B is very simple to use. For this reason it has a variety of applications, particularly when the testing of hypothesis H is conducted on a large sample.

In conclusion it might be worth while to say a few words about both tests. They can be used in two cases:

1 — when all the parameters of the distribution are known and we are checking only its shape;

2 — when we are testing a simple hypothesis that the population is two-dimensional and normal, with given parameters.

---

[1] Since, as a result of combining the last two classes in Table 1, we now have only three instead of four classes.

TABLE 2

PARAMETERS P_1 AND P_2 AS FUNCTIONS OF ϱ

ϱ	$p_1 = \dfrac{1}{4} + \dfrac{\text{arc sin } \varrho}{2\pi}$	$p_2 = \dfrac{1}{4} - \dfrac{\text{arc sin } \varrho}{2\pi}$
0·98	0·468	0·032
0·96	0·456	0·044
0·94	0·444	0·056
0·92	0·436	0·064
0·90	0·428	0·072
0·88	0·422	0·078
0·86	0·415	0·085
0·84	0·409	0·091
0·82	0·403	0·097
0·80	0·398	0·102
0·75	0·386	0·114
0·70	0·373	0·127
0·65	0·363	0·137
0·60	0·352	0·148
0·55	0·342	0·158
0·50	0·333	0·167
0·45	0·325	0·175
0·40	0·315	0·185
0·35	0·307	0·193
0·30	0·298	0·202
0·25	0·290	0·210
0·20	0·282	0·218
0·15	0·275	0·225
0·10	0·266	0·234
0·05	0·258	0·242

The verification of hypothesis H by both tests jointly should be carried out in two stages (as in two-stage sequence analysis). In the first stage we use test B. If it provides grounds for rejecting hypothesis H, the analysis is finished. If test B does not enable us to reject hypothesis H, we move on to the second stage, i.e. we apply test A.

4.2. Checking the hypothesis that the regression lines in general population Ω are straight lines

4.2.1. General comments

As we said in 1.2.5., the most difficult problem in the process of estimating regression parameters in a general population on the basis of a random sample taken from the population, is a proper choice of the approximation function. The amount of information that we have when we make such a choice is usually small: as a rule, all we have are the numerical data from the sample and the scatter diagram. From the distribution of the points on the scatter diagram we attempt *to guess* to which class the function appearing in the regression equation of the general population belongs. The word "guess" reflects very well the *idea* behind this procedure. When searching for this class we are groping in the dark. We cannot state anything; we can only guess. In this guessing the information supplied by the sample is useful and helpful: *it allows us to formulate a statistical* hypothesis that the function appearing in the regression equation *belongs to a certain class of functions*. The data from *the sample enable us to test this hypothesis*.

In this section we shall discuss the methods of testing the hypothesis that the *regression equation is a linear function*, i.e. that

$$g(x) = ax + \beta.$$

This hypothesis we shall denote by the symbol H_L. In this case

$$H_L = H[g(x) = ax + \beta].$$

The verification of this hypothesis is of great practical importance: as long as there are no grounds for rejecting hypothesis H_L we can consider that the regression lines in the general population are straight lines. No other statistical hypothesis will be better than hypothesis H_L; therefore we can abandon them all and retain to hypothesis H_L. The acceptance of some other hypothesis, even if it is equivalent to hypothesis H_L from the statistical point of view, results in serious inconveniences connected with dealing with a regression curve instead of a regression line and thus with the necessity of determining the parameters of a curve instead of those a line.

In the literature on the subject we can easily find (e.g. see [16], p. 397) a description of methods of testing hypothesis H_L by a large sample. In practice, however, it is often necessary to test this hypothesis on the basis of a small sample. In 4.2.2. we propose a test which enables the verification of hypothesis H_L when the sample is small. In the following item we describe, after Barkowski and Smirnow, a method of testing hypothesis H_L in a large sample.

4.2.2. Testing hypothesis H_L in a smal l sample by a run test

Hypothesis H_L can be verified by a run test. We shall describe this test briefly.

Let x_1, x_2, ..., x_n denote the realization of random variable X determined on the basis of the elements of general population Ω, and let $F(x)$ denote the distribution of variable X. If ω is a sample composed of n items and taken from Ω, then x_1, x_2, ..., x_n can be treated as the values of items selected for the sample (by "the values of items" we mean the actual values of random variable X corresponding to particular items of the sample). In repeated sampling, the values drawn may be treated as the realization of a finite sequence of variables X_1, X_2, ..., X_n, corresponding to the numbers of the items of sample ω. If the sample is random, then

1) random variables X_1, X_2, ..., X_n are independent;

2) they have the same distribution.

In this case

$$P(x_1, x_2, ..., x_n) = P(x_1) . P(x_2), ..., P(x_n).$$ (1)

The probability $P(x_1, x_2, ..., x_n)$ is not dependent upon the order of the variables. It follows that if sample ω is random then the $n!$ permutations formed from the numbers $x_1, x_2, ..., x_n$ have the same probability of occurrence.

Suppose that we have a sequence of n items composed exclusively of elements A and B. Here is an example of such a sequence:

$$A, A, A, B, A, B, B, A, B, A.$$ (2)

We have here $n = 10$ items, among which there are $n_1 = 6$ elements A, and $n_2 = 4$ elements B. Each sub-sequence with the largest possible number of items of the same kind is called *a run*. The number K of items comprising a given run is called *the length of the run*. Both the length of the run K and the number of runs R are random variables. The distributions of these variables are known. This enables us to test the hypothesis that sample ω was taken at random. Below we show a table taken from [16], p. 340. (A more detailed discussion of the problems related to run theory can be found in Chapter XIII of [20].) This table helps to verify the hypothesis by a run test. Symbol R_K appearing at the heading of the second column denotes the total number of runs with lengths not less than K; symbol R_{1K} denotes the number of runs composed of elements A, of length no less than K, and R_{2K} denotes the number of runs composed of elements B of length no less than K. In the table are given the maximum values of the number of observations n which satisfy one of the inequalities shown at the head of the second, third or fourth column, with probability less than 0·05. The method of using the run test described above for the verification of hypothesis H_L will be explained by an example.

TABLE 1
THE RUN TEST

Length of run K	The greatest number of observations n for which the probability of satisfying the inequalities shown below is less than 0·05		
	$R_K \geqslant 1$	and $\begin{array}{l} R_{1K} \geqslant 1 \\ R_{2K} \geqslant 1 \end{array}$	$R_{1K} \geqslant 1$
5	10	16	10
6	14	32	18
7	22	64	28
8	34	120	48
9	54	230	80
10	86		130
11	140		230
12	230		420

Example 1. Table 2 contains statistical data collected in a Wrocław brewery. The monthly production of beer in hectolitres is given in column x, and the cost of labour in zlotys in column y.

TABLE 2
BEER PRODUCTION AND LABOUR COSTS IN A WROCŁAW BREWERY

No	x	y	No	x	y
1	1,225	2,712,505	12	8,488	3,418,286
2	5,584	2,528,475	13	13,103	4,127,280
3	6,520	3,121,262	14	14,472	4,136,483
4	11,429	3,393,046	15	19,506	4,722,553
5	13,707	3,754,896	16	20,017	4,662,901
6	11,033	3,922,740	17	19,328	5,740,375
7	12,891	4,171,386	18	19,713	5,301,217
8	14,136	4,523,888	19	13,563	4,801,669
9	13,303	4,475,384	20	10,408	4,554,512
10	9,465	3,851,908	21	8,805	4,090,115
11	7,277	3,400,815	22	10,683	4,093,417

There is a relationship between the cost of labour and production. The regression line is a statistical expression of this relationship. The scatter diagram shown in Graph 1 suggests that the regression line is a straight line. This supposition may be treated as hypothesis H_L.

GRAPH 1.

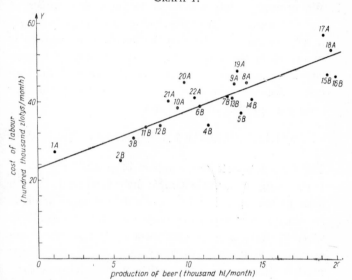

.The consecutive stages of the verification of this hypothesis are stated below.

1. Assuming that hypothesis H_L is true we estimate (by any method) the parameters of the regression line. In our example the equation of this line is:

$$y = 23 \cdot 8 + 0 \cdot 141x^1,$$

where the coefficient $b = 23 \cdot 8$ is measured in hundred thousand zlotys per month and the coefficient $a = 0 \cdot 141$ in hundred thousand zlotys per hectolitre.

---

[1] Computation Table is shown in the Appendix, p. 217.

11*

2. We denote by A the event that a point lies *above the regression line*, and by B the event that a point lies *below* this line. Points lying directly on the line are not taken into consideration. In practice this last event has no chance of being realized since in cases of continuous variables its probability is zero.

3. We arrange points according to increasing values of the abscissa. On the assumption that hypothesis H_L is true we can consider that the deviations of particular points from the line $y = 23 \cdot 8 + 0 \cdot 141x$ *are of random character and do not depend upon the order* of the succession of the points. In our example the points are arranged in the following order:

1,2,3,11,12,21,10,20,22,6,4,7,13,9,19,5,8,14,17,15,18,16.

The figures denote the numbers of points in Table 2. It may happen that in a sample there are points on both sides of the regression line, but with the same abscissa. In practice this is possible only when the abscissa X of variable (X,Y) is a discrete variable. In this case, however, the verification of hypothesis H_L is no longer needed and therefore we shall not consider this case.

4. Using the accepted arrangement of the points, we write the sequence of the realized events A and B. In our example the following sequence of events has been obtained:

$A,B,B,B,B,A,A,A,A,B,B,B,B,A,A,B,A,B,A,B,A,B.$

5. We find the maximum length of run K and, using Table 1, we analyse whether there are grounds for rejecting hypothesis H_L at the level of significance $a = 0 \cdot 05$. We reject this hypothesis when the test shows that the deviations of the points from the regression line are not

random, but that the points show a certain tendency in their location above or below the line. In our example

$$n = 22, \qquad K = 4.$$

Using Table 1 we can state that there are no grounds for rejecting hypothesis H_L.

When the sample is small, the testing of hypothesis H_L by a run test is very convenient since, as a rule, there are no computations involved other than those related to the determination of regression parameters. Checking whether a point lies below or above the regression line is done from the graph. To avoid difficulties the scale of the graph has to be properly selected. If a point *on the graph* lies exactly on the regression line (on Graph 1 — points No. 6 and 11) we have to make appropriate calculations and check whether this point really lies on the regression line or whether it only *appears* to be located directly on the line because of the scale used in the graph and the drawing technique (upon which the thickness of the line and the size of the point depends). If random variable (X, Y) is continuous and if the sample is small and the graph sufficiently large, then it is seldom necessary to carry out computations to check whether a point lies on the line or close to it.

4.2.3. *Testing hypothesis H_L in a large sample by Fisher's test*

The verification of hypothesis H_L by a run test becomes troublesome when the sample is very large. In such cases the checking of each point, whether below or above the regression line, takes too much time even if we do not make calculations but use only the graph.

The verification of hypothesis H_L in a large sample can be done by Fisher's test F. It can be proved that the random variable

$$\frac{(n-l)\,(\bar{\eta}_y^2 - r^2)}{(l-2)\,(1-\bar{\eta}_y^2)} \qquad (1)$$

has the distribution F with the number of the degrees of freedom $k_1 = l-2$ and $k_2 = n-l$. In formula (1) symbol $\bar{\eta}_y^2$ denotes an estimate of parameter η_y^2 on the basis of the sample (see 1.2.8.); n, as usual, denotes the size of the sample, and l the number of values that variable X assumes in the contingency table (in other words l is the number of rows in this table).

A detailed description as to how test F should be used to verify hypothesis H_L, together with a numerical example, can be found in [16], p. 397.

4.3. *An analysis of the significance of regression parameters*

The regression coefficient in a sample is a random variable with its own distribution, its expected value and variance. Bartlett has shown (see [4]) that if the distribution of the random variable (X,Y) is normal[1], then the variable

$$t' = \frac{S_1\sqrt{n-2}}{S_2\sqrt{1-r^2}}\,(a_{21} - \alpha_{21}) \qquad (1)$$

has Student's distribution with $n-2$ degrees of freedom[2].

---

[1] We shall mention in passing that the Bartlett test can only be used if the distribution of variables (X,Y) is normal. That is one of the reasons why in 4.1. we gave two tests for verifying the hypothesis that the distribution of the variable (X,Y) is normal.

[2] Tables for Student's distribution are given at the end of the book.

In formula (1)

$$S_1 = \sqrt{\frac{1}{n} \sum_i (x_i - \bar{x})^2}, \qquad S_2 = \sqrt{\frac{1}{n} \sum_i (y_i - \bar{y})^2},$$

$$a_{21} = \frac{\sum_i (x_i - \bar{x})(y_i - \bar{y})}{\sum_i (x_i - \bar{x})^2}.$$

By elementary transformations we can show that

$$t' = \frac{S_1 \sqrt{n-2}}{S_{21}} (a_{21} - \alpha_{21}), \tag{2}$$

where

$$S_{21} = \sqrt{\frac{\sum_i (y_i - \bar{y})^2 - a_{21} \sum_i (x_i - \bar{x})(y_i - \bar{y})}{n}}.$$

The knowledge of the distribution of variable t' enables us to determine the confidence region which will cover the unknown value of parameter α_{21} with probability a. Knowing the distribution of variable t' we can write that

$$P\left\{ a_{21} - \frac{t' \cdot S_{21}}{S_1 \sqrt{n-2}} < \alpha_{21} < a_{21} + \frac{t' \cdot S_{21}}{S_1 \sqrt{n-2}} \right\} = a. \tag{3}$$

We can also prove that the variable

$$t'' = \frac{\sqrt{n-2}}{S_{21}} (b_{20} - \beta_{20}) \tag{4}$$

has Student's distribution with $n-2$ degrees of freedom. Hence

$$P\left\{ b_{20} - \frac{t'' \cdot S_{21}}{\sqrt{n-2}} < \beta_{20} < b_{20} + \frac{t'' \cdot S_{21}}{\sqrt{n-2}} \right\} = a. \tag{5}$$

In formulae (4) and (5) the parameter $b_{20} = \bar{y} - a_{21}\bar{x}$. It can also be proved that the variable

$$t = \frac{\sqrt{n-2}}{S_{21} \cdot \sqrt{1 + \frac{(x - \bar{x})^2}{S_1^2}}} \cdot (\tilde{y} - \hat{y}) \qquad (6)$$

has Student's distribution with $n-2$ degrees of freedom. Therefore

$$P\left\{ \tilde{y} - \frac{t \cdot S_{21} \sqrt{1 + \frac{(x - \bar{x})^2}{S_i^2}}}{\sqrt{n-2}} < \hat{y} < \tilde{y} + \right.$$

$$\left. + \frac{t \cdot S_{21} \sqrt{1 + \frac{(x - \bar{x})^2}{S_1^2}}}{\sqrt{n-2}} \right\} = \alpha. \qquad (7)$$

We shall show the formal relationship between formulae (2) and (4), and formula (7). Let us consider the regression line equation in the sample

$$\tilde{y} = ax + b,$$

where

$$a = \frac{\sum (x - \bar{x})(y - \bar{y})}{\sum (x - \bar{x})^2}, \qquad b = \bar{y} - a\bar{x}.$$

Let us assume that

$$S^2(a) = \frac{S_{21}^2}{S_1^2(n-2)}, \qquad S^2(b) = \frac{S_{21}^2}{n-2},$$

$$S^2(\tilde{y}) = \frac{S_{21}^2}{n-2}\left[1 + \frac{(x - \bar{x})^2}{S_1^2} \right]. \qquad (8)$$

Hence

$$S^2(\bar{y}) = \frac{(x - \bar{x})^2 \, S_{21}^2}{S_1^2 \, (n-2)} + \frac{S_{21}^2}{(n-2)}$$

$$= (x - \bar{x})^2 . \, S^2(a) + S^2(b) = S^2[a(x - \bar{x})] + S^2(b). \qquad (9)$$

Therefore, on the basis of (8) and (9)

$$t' = \frac{a_{21} - \alpha_{21}}{S(a_{21})}, \qquad (10)$$

$$t'' = \frac{b_{20} - \beta_{20}}{S(b_{21})}, \qquad (11)$$

$$t = \frac{\bar{y} - \hat{y}}{S(\bar{y})}. \qquad (12)$$

All comments concerning the regression parameters of Y on X also apply to the regression parameters of X on Y.

Example 1. The scatter diagram on Graph 1 shows the relationship between the average monthly expenditures for consumption and the average monthly income of twenty four-member families drawn from among four-member families included in family budget studies in Lower Silesia. The statistical data on which the diagram is based come from Table 2 in 3.2.2.

GRAPH 1.

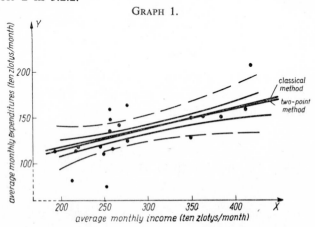

The two straight lines shown on Graph 1 are regression lines determined by the classical method and the two-point method. The positions of the two lines do not differ much. The equation of the regression line determined by the method of least squares is

$$\tilde{y} = 47 + 0 \cdot 31x,$$

and the equation of the regression line determined by the two-point method is

$$\tilde{y} = 55 + 0 \cdot 28x.[1]$$

The equations of the two continuous curves shown on Graph 1 are expressed by the formula

$$\tilde{y} + \frac{t \cdot S_{21} \sqrt{1 + \frac{(x - \bar{x})^2}{S_i^2}}}{n - 2}. \tag{13}$$

In our example

$$\begin{aligned}
\tilde{y} &= 47 + 0 \cdot 31x, \\
S_i^2 &= 4{,}269, \\
S_{21} &= 20 \cdot 69, \\
\bar{x} &= 281, \\
n &= 20.
\end{aligned}$$

Thus the equation of the continuous curve *located above* the regression lines and corresponding to the value $t = 1$ will assume the following form:

$$y = 47 + 0 \cdot 31x + 20 \cdot 69 \cdot \frac{\sqrt{1 + \frac{(x - 281)^2}{4{,}269}}}{\sqrt{18}},$$

---

[1] The computation table is shown in the Appendix p. 218.

and the equation of the continuous curve *located below* the regression lines and corresponding to the value $t = -1$ is expressed by the formula

$$y = 47 + 0.31x - 20.69 \cdot \frac{\sqrt{1 + \dfrac{(x - 281)^2}{4,269}}}{\sqrt{18}}.$$

Curves (13) determine the *confidence region* which will cover the regression line in the general population Ω with probability a. For $a = 0.98$ with 18 degrees of freedom, we find in Student's distribution table:

$$t = 2.55.$$

The two interrupted curves on Graph 1 are curves (13) for $t = 2.55$[1].

Using the confidence region we can decide whether the position of the regression line obtained by the method of least squares differs *significantly* from the position of the regression line obtained by the two-point method. Let us denote by H_r the statistical hypothesis that there is only a *random* difference between the position of the regression line determined by the method of least squares on the basis of statistical data from sample ω and the position of the regression line obtained on the basis of the same data by the two-point method. To test hypothesis H_r we have to select a number a and accordingly draw two lines determining the confidence region. We reject hypothesis H_r when the line determined by the two-point method intersects one of the curves determining the confidence region. We can see from the graph that in our example there are no grounds for rejecting hy-

---

[1] See the Appendix p. 219.

pothesis H_r since the line determined by the two-point method does not intersect either of the two broken curves drawn on Graph 1. These lines correspond to the confidence coefficient $\alpha = 0.98$.

We know that if a regression I line in a general population is a straight line the regression parameters in the population calculated by the two methods will be the same. This means that the estimates of regression parameters obtained from the sample by the method of least squares and by the two-point method should not show any significant difference if the assumption is true that the regression line of the population is a straight line. It follows that the verification of hypothesis H_r is equivalent to the verification of hypothesis H_L. In our example hypothesis H_r has not been rejected. It is easy to find out (using the run test described in 4.2.2.) that there are also no grounds for rejecting hypothesis H_L.

The verification of hypothesis H_L by the determination of the confidence region for the regression line is too cumbersome. Let us remember, however, that the regression lines of the sample determined by both methods go through point $(\bar{x}, \bar{y})$. Therefore, instead of checking whether the positions of the two regression lines differ significantly from one another, it is sufficient to find out whether their slopes differ significantly. To do this we proceed as follows.

We select number α and determine the confidence region for $a_{21 \text{ class}}$ according to formula (3). Then we check whether $a_{21 \text{ point}}$[1] lies within this region. We reject hypothesis H_L *when $a_{21 \text{ point}}$ lies outside the confidence region, i.e. is in the critical area.*

---

[1] Let us remember that $a_{21 \text{ class}}$ is the regression coefficient obtained by the classical method, and $a_{21 \text{ point}}$ denotes the regression coefficient obtained by the two-point method (see List of Symbols at the end of the book).

In our example we have:

$$a_{21 \text{ class}} = 0 \cdot 31,$$
$$a_{21 \text{ point}} = 0 \cdot 28,$$
$$S_{21} = 20 \cdot 69,$$
$$S_1^2 = 4,269, \text{ hence } s_1 = 65,$$
$$a = 0 \cdot 98,$$
$$t' = 2 \cdot 55,$$
$$n = 20.$$

Therefore

$$0 \cdot 31 - \frac{20 \cdot 69 \cdot 2 \cdot 55}{4 \cdot 3 \cdot 65} < a_{21} < 0 \cdot 31 + \frac{20 \cdot 69 \cdot 2 \cdot 55}{4 \cdot 3 \cdot 65}$$

or

$$0 \cdot 12 < a_{21} < 0 \cdot 50.$$

Since

$$0 \cdot 12 < a_{21 \text{ point}} = 0 \cdot 28 < 0 \cdot 50,$$

the slopes of the two lines are not significantly different so that there are no grounds for rejecting hypothesis H_L.

The application of the two-point method to the verification of hypothesis H_L is very convenient since there are few extra computations involved. If we have made all calculations required to determine parameter $a_{21 \text{ class}}$ the determination of parameter $a_{21 \text{ point}}$ is simple because most of the calculations needed for the classical method can be used in the two-point method.

We can see from this example that the two-point method is not only useful for estimating the regression parameters, but can also be applied to the verification of hypothesis H_L.

Example 2. Table 1 contains data from monthly reports on the production of beer in hundreds of hectolitres (x) and the cost of electric power in thousands of zlotys (y). The figures follow the chronological order.

TABLE 1

BEER PRODUCTION AND POWER COSTS IN A WROCŁAW
BREWERY

No	x	y	No	x	y
1	12	292	11	73	459
2	56	308	12	62	446
3	65	388	13	195	414
4	114	388	14	200	463
5	137	517	15	193	448
6	110	545	16	197	449
7	129	536	17	136	435
8	141	536	18	104	373
9	133	561	19	88	361
10	95	512	20	107	366

The data from this table were used for Graph 2.

GRAPH 2.

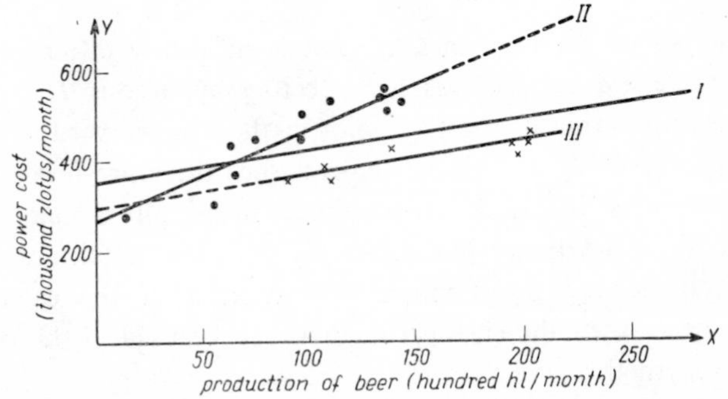

There are three straight lines on this graph. The line with
the equation $y = 359 + 0.69x$ was determined from *full*
statistical material, i.e. from the data pertaining to *all*
points. We shall call it line I. At first glance this line
does not arouse any doubts. Let us note, however, that
8 consecutive points (marked on the graph by crosses) are

located *below* the regression line. These points correspond to the data for the *last* eight months shown in Table 1. An event consisting of 8 *consecutive* points from among 20 points distributed *at random* on both sides of the regression line and located on one side of the line, has a small probability of occurrence. A run test indicates that the line with equation $y = 359 + 0.69x$ cannot be considered as a regression line. For this reason the data contained in Table 1 should be divided into two parts[1]. In the first part the first 12 observations are included. The equation of the regression line based on these data is $y = 277 + 1.93x$. Let us call it line II. The second part comprises the remaining 8 observations. The equation of the corresponding regression line is $y = 300 + 0.75x$. We shall call it line III. Using formula (6) we can discover that the *position of line II differs significantly from that of line III*. This much information has been provided by a formal analysis of the data shown in Table 1. Let us now comment upon the economic aspect of the problem. The efforts of the factory personnel to reduce the cost of production were effective: the cost of electric power was substantially lowered. Success came imperceptibly. The daily efforts of each worker to save electric power finally had a visible cumulative effect over a period of several months. The *nature* of the relationship between the cost of power and production[2] changed significantly. The variable part of the cost of electric power was lowered. In the first 12 months this cost amounted to 19.3 zlotys/hl.; in the next 8 months it only amounted to 7.5 zlotys/hl. This is a very important achievement by the workers of the enterprise.

Let us here make the following comment: an analysis as to whether the position of the regression line in population Ω_1

---

[1] See the Appendix — computation table on pp. 220–222.

[2] Let us note in passing that we could not learn about this relationship without the assistance of correlation analysis.

differs significantly from the position of the regression line in population Ω_2 is possible only when the hypothesis is true that the standard errors of estimates (see 1.2.7.) in Ω_1, and Ω_2 are the same. This hypothesis can be verified by Fisher's F test, or (especially when the sample is small) by Sadowski's test [48].

4.4. *An analysis of the significance of the correlation coefficient*

If the distribution of the random variable (X,Y) defined on the elements of the general population Ω is normal and if the correlation coefficient ϱ of the population is close to zero, then, for a sufficiently large n, the distribution of the correlation coefficient r in sample ω drawn from Ω does not differ much from a normal distribution with parameters

$$E(r) = \varrho,$$

$$V(r) = \frac{1 - \varrho^2}{\sqrt{n - 1}}.$$

Therefore, for ϱ close to zero and for a large n, the distribution of the random variable

$$t_r = \frac{r - \varrho}{1 - \varrho^2} \cdot \sqrt{n - 1} \tag{1}$$

is close to normal $N(0,1)$ (see [28][1]).

It can also be proved that if $\varrho = 0$ then the random variable

$$t = \frac{r}{1 - r^2} \cdot \sqrt{n - 2} \tag{2}$$

has Student's distribution with $n - 2$ degrees of freedom. Thus we can easily test the hypothesis that $\varrho = 0$. We shall denote this hypothesis by H_0. In this case

$$H_0 = H(\varrho = 0).$$

---

[1] A. Hald: *Statistical Theory with Engineering Applications*, New York, 1952, p. 608.

In practice it is often necessary to test hypothesis H_0; therefore we shall illustrate below the procedure involved in checking this hypothesis.

Fisher, who studied the distribution of the correlation coefficient, obtained interesting results with wide practical implications, by introducing the variable

$$z = \frac{1}{2} \ln \frac{1+r}{1-r} \approx 1 \cdot 513 \log \frac{1+r}{1-r}, \tag{3}$$

where $-1 \leqslant r \leqslant 1$; $-\infty < z < 0$.

In formula (3) ln denotes the natural logarithm, and log stands for the logarithm to the base 10.

As n increases the distribution z converges rapidly to the normal distribution. Since

$$E(z) \approx \frac{1}{2} \ln \frac{1+\varrho}{1-\varrho} + \frac{\varrho}{2(n-1)}, \tag{4}$$

and

$$V(z) \approx \frac{1}{n-3}, \tag{5}$$

then the distribution of the random variable

$$t_z = [z - E(z)] \sqrt{n-3} \tag{6}$$

is close to the normal distribution $N(0,1)$. In this case

$$P\left\{ z - \frac{t_z}{\sqrt{n-3}} < E(z) < z + \frac{t_z}{\sqrt{n-3}} \right\} = a, \tag{7}$$

where $0 < a < 1$.

Knowing the confidence region for $E(z)$ we can easily write the confidence region for $E(r) = \varrho$. Let us denote

$$z_1 = z - \frac{t_z}{\sqrt{n-3}}, \quad z_2 = z + \frac{t_z}{\sqrt{n-3}}.$$

In this case

$$P\left\{ z_1 < \frac{1}{2} \ln \frac{1+\varrho}{1-\varrho} + \frac{\varrho}{2(n-1)} < z_2 \right\} = a.$$

If we omit the second component of the sum between the inequality signs $\left(\text{since it is small in comparison with} \dfrac{1}{\sqrt{n-3}}\right)$, then after elementary transformation we obtain

$$P\left\{\frac{e^{2z_1}-1}{e^{2z_1}+1} < \varrho < \frac{e^{2z_2}-1}{e^{2z_2}+1}\right\} \approx \alpha. \qquad (8)$$

The double inequality within the brackets determines the confidence region for ϱ.

Let us now illustrate by an example the verification of hypothesis H_0.

Example 1. Table 1 contains the data on the average monthly income (x) and the average monthly expenditures on drink (y) for 30 four-member families drawn from among four-member families included in family budget studies in Lower Silesia.

TABLE 1

MONTHLY INCOMES AND MONTHLY EXPENDITURES ON DRINK
FOR 30 FOUR-MEMBER FAMILIES

No	x	y	No	x	y	No	x	y
1	2,568	42	11	2,563	15	21	9,263	47
2	2,538	42	12	4,058	71	22	3,639	76
3	2,491	46	13	2,577	71	23	4,861	231
4	3,442	34	14	2,129	39	24	4,918	78
5	2,462	29	15	3,450	33	25	2,607	82
6	4,111	36	16	2,734	68	26	3,904	119
7	2,170	134	17	2,515	118	27	3,594	71
8	2,191	74	18	2,251	27	28	3,884	134
9	3,586	153	19	2,544	17	29	3,110	146
10	3,777	210	20	1,940	32	30	5,388	54

The scatter diagram shown on Graph 1 is based on the data from this table.

GRAPH 1.

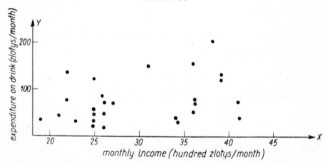

The distribution of the points on the scatter diagram suggests that the relationship between the expenditures on drink and the size of income is very weak. In economic language this means that the want called "drink" is fully satisfied in Poland.

This rather regrettable fact is generally known and statistics serve only to confirm it. It follows from the calculations that the correlation coefficient between the expenditures on drink and income is 0·19. Let us formulate the hypothesis H_0 that the correlation coefficient $\varrho = 0$. To test this hypothesis let us calculate the value of t according to formula (2). We have

$$t = \frac{0 \cdot 19}{1 - (0 \cdot 19)^2} \cdot \sqrt{28} \approx 1 \cdot 04.$$

In Student's distribution tables for $\alpha = 0 \cdot 05$ with 28 degrees of freedom, we find that $t_0 = 2 \cdot 045$. Since

$$t = 1 \cdot 04 < t_0 = 2 \cdot 045,$$

there are no grounds for rejecting the hypothesis H_0 that the correlation coefficient between the expenditures on drink and income equals zero.

5. THE TRANSFORMATION OF CURVILINEAR INTO LINEAR REGRESSION

It may happen that the points on the scatter diagram are so distributed that we should reject the hypothesis H_L (see 4.2.) stating that the correlation is linear. We can then proceed in one of the following two ways: either by determining the parameters of the segments of straight lines forming a broken line or by selecting a family of curves and determining the parameters of one of the curves belonging to this family.

We shall not discuss here the method of determining the broken line since this can be reduced to the determination of the parameters of a linear regression, but we shall deal with certain cases of curvilinear regression. Suppose that the stochastic relationship between variables x and y can be well described by a function which is graphically presented as a curve. Let us consider a family of such functions; by appropriate transformations they can be reduced to the linear form:

$$z = \lambda v + \gamma, \tag{1}$$

where $z = z(y)$, $v = v(x)$ and λ and γ are constants. Table 1 shows the most commonly used transformations and the functions that can be obtained by them. In equation (1) there are *two* parameters. However, it may happen that for the approximating curve to describe properly the distribution of the points on the diagram, the equation of the curve must be a function with more than two parameters. Then, of course, linear transformation cannot be used. In economic research, however, it is seldom necessary to use the type of function having more than two parameters.

TABLE I

SOME EXAMPLES OF LINEAR TRANSFORMATION FUNCTIONS

No	$y = g(x)$	Type of function	z	v	λ	γ	$z = \lambda v + \gamma$	Graph No
1	$y = \dfrac{1}{ax+b}$	hyperbola	$\dfrac{1}{y}$	x	a	b	$\dfrac{1}{y} = ax + b$	1
2	$y = \dfrac{a}{x} + b$	"	y	$\dfrac{1}{x}$	a	b	$y = \dfrac{a}{x} + b$	
3	$y = \dfrac{x}{a+bx}$	"	$\dfrac{1}{y}$	$\dfrac{1}{x}$	a	b	$\dfrac{1}{y} = \dfrac{a}{x} + b$	
4	$y = \dfrac{cx}{ax+b}$ where $c = a \cdot b$	"	$\dfrac{1}{y}$	$\dfrac{1}{x}$	$\dfrac{1}{a}$	$\dfrac{1}{b}$	$\dfrac{1}{y} = \dfrac{1}{ax} + \dfrac{1}{b}$	
5	$y = b \cdot a^x$	exponential	$\ln y$	x	$\ln a$	$\ln b$	$\ln y = x\ln a + \ln b$	2
6	$y = b \cdot e^{ax}$	"	$\ln y$	x	a	$\ln b$	$\ln y = ax + \ln b$	3
7	$y = bx^a$	power	$\ln y$	$\ln x$	a	$\ln b$	$\ln y = a\ln x + \ln b$	4
8	$y = a\ln x + b$	logarithmic	y	$\ln x$	a	b	$y = a\ln x + b$	5
9	$y = a\sin x + b$	trigonometric	y	$\sin x$	a	b	$y = a\sin x + b$	
10	$y = a\tan x + b$	"	y	$\tan x$	a	b	$y = a\tan x + b$	
11	$y = \dfrac{1}{ae^{-x} + b}$	logistic	$\dfrac{1}{y}$	e^{-x}	a	b	$\dfrac{1}{y} = ae^{-x} + b$	6

The functions reviewed in Table 1 have many applications in econometrics. For instance, in studies on demand we deal with hyperbolic relationships (see 2.2.3.). A parabola, an exponential curve and a logarithmic curve are used in the theory of wants (see 2.2.1.). In demographic research exponential curves are most frequently used (this will be discussed in Example 1). A hyperbola is used in the theory of costs (see 2.2.4.). To the analysis of time series various functions are applied, the most frequently used after linear function being trigonometric functions and the function that is geometrically represented by a "logistic curve".

Winkler's work [61] provides a review of the more important functional relationships in economics. For this reason the book is well worth reading. In studying techno-economic relationships (see 2.2.6.) and in determining distribution curves (see 2.2.2., Graph 1) various functions are used. However, in these cases, too, the functions most frequently employed are those shown in Table 1.

Linear transformation is used mainly because it enables us to satisfy the conditions required by the Markoff Theorem.

If the parameters of any approximating function obtained by formula (1) are determined by the method of least squares, then we know from the Markoff Theorem that these parameters are consistent, unbiased and the most effective estimates.

Linear transformation is also useful because it considerably simplifies calculations. This is of great practical importance and, therefore, we shall discuss this aspect in greater detail. As we know, in order to determine the values of constant parameters in the equation of the approximating function $y = g(x)$ by the method of least squares the partial derivatives have to be calculated for the expression

$$\sum [y_i - g(x_i)]^2 \quad (i = 1, 2, ..., n).$$

GRAPH 1.　　　　　GRAPH 2.

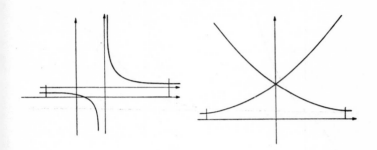

GRAPH 3.

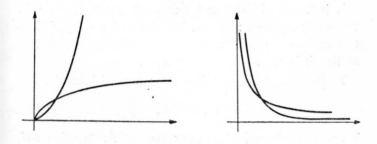

GRAPH 4.　　　　　GRAPH 5.

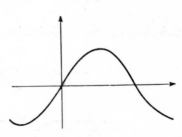

GRAPH 6.   GRAPH 7.

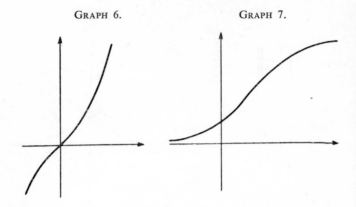

This is to be equated to zero and the set of normal equations so obtained then solved.

It is usually difficult and sometimes impossible to solve this set by algebraic methods. The application of approximation methods further complicates the computation procedure so that it is of little value in practice.

To illustrate, let us consider the exponential function

$$g(x) = ba^x.$$

We want to determine the parameters of this function and, therefore, we want

$$S = \sum_i [y_i - ba^{x_i}]^2 \text{ to be a minimum.}$$

Calculate the partial derivatives

$$\frac{\partial S}{\partial b} = -2 \sum_i [y_i - ba^{x_i}]a^{x_i},$$

$$\frac{\partial S}{\partial a} = -2 \sum_i [y_i - ba^{x_i}]ba^{x_i-1} \cdot x_i.$$

Equate them to zero:

$$\sum_i a^{x_i} y_i - b \sum_i a^{2x_i} = 0,$$

$$b \sum_i x_i y_i a^{x_i-1} - b^2 \sum_i x_i a^{2x_i-1} = 0.$$

As we can see, there are difficulties in solving this set of normal equations (containing only two unknowns). These difficulties disappear when we apply linear transformation. Thus we calculate ln y_i and minimize the expression

$$S = \sum_i [z_i - \lambda v_i - \gamma]^2,$$

where

$$z_i = \ln y_i, \qquad v_i = x_i,$$
$$\lambda = \ln a, \qquad \gamma = \ln b.$$

From the solution of the set of normal equations we obtain the known formulae

$$\gamma = \bar{z} - \lambda \bar{v},$$

$$\lambda = \frac{\sum_i (z - \bar{z})(v - \bar{v})}{\sum_i (v - \bar{v})^2}.$$

Having the values of λ and γ we can calculate parameters a and b without difficulty.

It can be seen from the above comments that there are good reasons why linear transformation should be used. We have to remember, however, that in spite of the fact that the computation is thus considerably facilitated, it is fairly difficult to determine the parameters of the regression line by the method of least squares. This is due to the fact that by performing the calculations on the numbers x_i and y_i required for linear transformation, we obtain three-, four,- or five-digit numbers which cannot be rounded off radically without endangering the accuracy of these calculations. Under these circumstances the two-point method is very useful because it enables us to determine the regression parameters without cumbersome computations. This method is used in the numerical examples given below.

Example 1.

TABLE 2

GROWTH OF POPULATION IN SWEDEN 1750–1935

Years	Population	t	x	$z = \ln x$
1750	1,780,678	1	178	5·18178
1760	1,925,248	2	193	5·25750
1770	2,042,574	3	204	5·31812
1780	2,118,281	4	212	5·35659
1790	2,187,732	5	219	5·38907
1800	2,347,303	6	235	5·45959
1810	2,396,351	7	240	5·48064
1820	2,584,690	8	258	5·55296
1830	2,888,082	9	289	5·66643
1840	3,138,887	10	314	5·74939
		$\Sigma = 55$		$\Sigma = 54·41207$
1850	3,482,541	11	348	5·85220
1860	3,859,728	12	386	5·95586
1870	4,168,525	13	417	6·03309
1880	4,565,668	14	457	6·12468
1890	4,784,981	15	478	6·16961
1900	5,136,441	16	514	6·24222
1910	5,522,403	17	552	6·31355
1920	5,904,489	18	590	6·38012
1930	6,142,191	19	614	6·41999
1935	6,250,506	19·5	625	6·43775
		$\Sigma = 154·5$		$\Sigma = 61·92907$
		$\Sigma = 209·5$		$\Sigma = 116·34114$

In Table 2 the population of Sweden is shown for 1750–1935 (see [61], p. 158). In column t the consecutive numbers of years are given, and in column x — the population figures rounded off to three significant digits.

Parameters λ and γ are calculated by formulae (7) and (8), 3.3.1.

We have

$$\bar{z}_{(2)} = \frac{61 \cdot 92907}{10} = 6 \cdot 192907,$$

$$\bar{z}_{(1)} = \frac{54 \cdot 41207}{10} = 5 \cdot 441207,$$

$$\bar{t}_{(2)} = \frac{154 \cdot 5}{10} = 15 \cdot 450000,$$

$$\bar{t}_{(1)} = \frac{55}{10} = 5 \cdot 500000,$$

$$\bar{z} = \frac{116 \cdot 34114}{20} = 5 \cdot 817557,$$

$$\bar{t} = \frac{209 \cdot 5}{20} = 10 \cdot 4800000,$$

$$\lambda = \frac{6 \cdot 192907 - 5 \cdot 441207}{15 \cdot 45 - 5 \cdot 5} \approx 0 \cdot 075548,$$

$$\gamma = \ln b = 5 \cdot 81756 - 0 \cdot 075548 \cdot 10 \cdot 48 \approx 5 \cdot 02582,$$

$$b = 148.$$

A straight line with the equation $z = 5 \cdot 02582 + 0 \cdot 075548v$ is shown on Graph 8. As we can see, it fits very well to the distribution of the points on the graph. These points show a clear linear tendency. Note that the points have been plotted in the coordinate system *voz* and not in the system *toz*, because Graph 8 shows the distribution of points after linear transformation. This transformation was needed for the determination of parameters *a* and *b*. After these parameters are found we can return to the original distribution, i.e. the distribution before transformation. This distribution, together with the regression line fitted to it, is shown on Graph 9, p. 189. As can be seen, an exponential curve well represents the dynamics of population growth in Sweden. A major deviation can be noticed only in the first and last years of the period studied. It can be seen from the graph that the parameters of the curve have been properly chosen and so it can be said that the dependence of the population growth in Sweden upon time, in the period 1750–1935, can be approximated by the exponential function with the equation

$$\tilde{x} = 148. \, e^{0.075548 \, t}.$$

The application of linear transformation enabled us to determine parameters *a* and *b* without difficulty; the known formulae for determining the parameters of the straight line were used. Substantial simplifications in the computation were also achieved by the application of the two-point method to the determination of the regression parameters.

GRAPH 8.

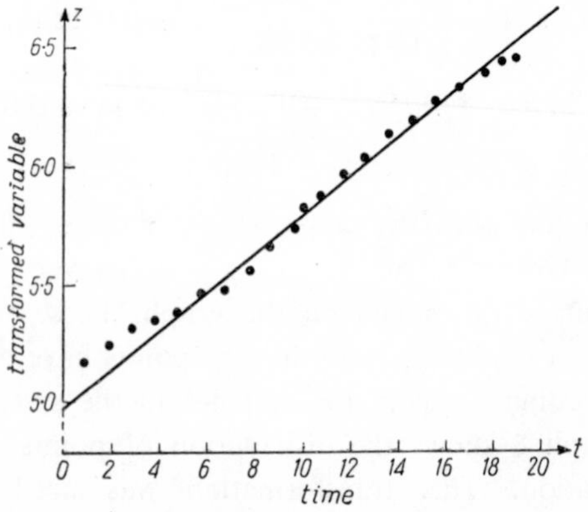

GRAPH 9.

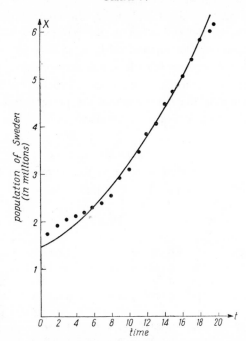

Example 2. W. Styś has noticed during his demographic studies that there is an interesting relationship between the number of children in peasant families and the size of farms possessed by these families. This relationship can be consider significant since it appears very clearly on the basis of abundant statistical data (the sample covers 8,505 families). The relationship noticed by Styś can very well be described by a power function. The equation of the regression line calculated by the method of least squares and with the application of a linear transformation (see [55]) is

$$\bar{y} = 5{\cdot}51 \ x^{0{\cdot}14}.$$

Since in linear transformation it is necessary to take logarithms which provide five-digit numbers and since the frequency of the distribution is expressed by numbers with three of four significant digits, the computations connected with the determination of the parameters of the regression curve by the method of least squares are cumbersome and time-consuming. Incomparably simpler calculations are required for the two-point method. To illustrate we shall compute the parameters of the power curve by this method. The data are taken from Table 3.

TABLE 3

NUMBER OF CHILDREN IN, AND FARMS OWNED BY, PEASANT FAMILIES

i	x	y	n_i	$v = \log x$	$z = \log y$	$n_i \cdot v$	$n_i z$
1	0·25	4·88	317	−0·6021	0·6884	− 190·8657	218·2228
2	0·75	5·20	658	−0·1249	0·7160	− 82·1842	471·1280
3	1·50	5·79	1,509	0·1761	0·7627	265·7349	1,150·9143
4	2·50	6·16	1,584	0·3979	0·7896	630·2736	1,250·7264
			$\Sigma = 4,068$			$\Sigma = 622·9586$	$\Sigma = 3,090·9915$
5	3·50	6·57	836	0·5441	0·8176	454·8676	683·5136
6	4·50	6·83	961	0·6532	0·8344	627·7252	801·8584
7	6·00	7·00	1,319	0·7782	0·8451	1,026·4458	1,114·6869
8	8·50	7·67	620	0·9294	0·8848	576·2280	548·5760
9	12·50	7·90	509	1·0969	0·8976	558·3221	456·8784
10	17·50	8·59	139	1·2430	0·9340	172·7770	129·8260
11	25·00	8·66	44	1·3979	0·9375	61·5076	41·2500
12	40·00	9·11	9	1·6021	0·9595	14·4189	8·6595
			$\Sigma = 4,437$			$\Sigma = 3,492·2922$	$\Sigma = 3,785·2488$

Variable Y denotes the average number of children born to a farmer of the previous generation and variable X stands for the size of the farm. Assuming that the relationship between variables X and Y is expressed by the formula

$$y = bx^a,$$

after using logarithms we get the linear expression:

$$z = \lambda v + \gamma,$$

where $z = \log y$, $v = \log x$, $\lambda = a$, $\gamma = \log b$.

It should be explained that the division of the sample ω into the two subgroups ω_1, and ω_2 required for the two-point method has been done in such a way as to make the frequencies of these subgroups as close to one another as possible. Because of the asymmetry of the distribution of variable (X,Y), subgroup ω_1 contains 4 classes of the frequency distribution, and subgroup ω_2, 8 classes.

Below are the calculations connected with the determination of the values of parameters λ and γ.

$$\bar{z}_{\langle 2 \rangle} = \frac{3{,}785}{4{,}437} = 0{\cdot}8531,$$

$$\bar{z}_{\langle 1 \rangle} = \frac{3{,}091}{4{,}068} = 0{\cdot}7598,$$

$$\bar{v}_{(2)} = \frac{3{,}492}{4{,}437} = 0{\cdot}7869,$$

$$\bar{v}_{(1)} = \frac{623}{4{,}068} = 0{\cdot}1531,$$

$$\lambda = \frac{0{\cdot}8531 - 0{\cdot}7598}{0{\cdot}7869 - 0{\cdot}1531} = 0{\cdot}147,$$

$$\gamma = 0{\cdot}8531 - 0{\cdot}147 \cdot 0{\cdot}7869 = 0{\cdot}7374.$$

Hence

$$a = 0{\cdot}147, \qquad b = 5{\cdot}46.$$

Therefore, the equation of the regression curve determined by the two-point method is

$$\tilde{y} = 5{\cdot}46 \; x^{0{\cdot}147}.$$

GRAPH 10.

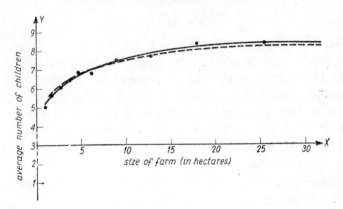

On Graph 10 a scatter diagram is shown with two regression curves determined by the classical method (broken line) and the two-point method (continuous line). It can be seen from the graph that both curves are good representations of the distribution of points on the graph. However, the determination of the regression curve by the two-point method is much easier and, therefore, this method turns out to be more useful in this example.

6. THE REGRESSION LINE AND THE TREND

6.1. *The definition of trend*[1]

Let us denote by Ω_t a collection of items composing a general population. To each item of this collection a value of the random variable X_t is assigned; it is known that its distribution depends on the time t. The relationship is such that

$$\hat{x} = E(X \mid t) = \psi(t), \tag{1}$$

where $\psi(t)$ is a function determined for at least those values of t that satisfy the inequality $0 \leqslant t \leqslant m$.

In the special case when $\psi(t)$ is linear, formula (1) assumes the following form:

$$\hat{x} = \alpha t + \beta, \tag{2}$$

where α and β are constants.

Let us denote by r and s two moments of time of which we know that $0 \leqslant r < s \leqslant m$. Points r and s determine a certain time interval whose length is $T = s - r$. Let us divide the length of time T into $n+1$ parts by points $t = 1, 2, ..., n$. These parts we shall call segments. At every moment of time t $(t = 1, 2, ..., n)$ we draw from population Ω_t and return to it $k_t \geqslant 1$ items, examine which values of random variable X_t correspond to these items and calculate the arithmetic means of these values. In this way we get n pairs of numbers $(1, \bar{x}_1)$, $(2, \bar{x}_2)$, ..., $(n, \bar{x}_n)$. *These numbers constitute a time series.* If function $\psi(t)$ is linear it is to be expected that if we represent

---

[1] Published in *Przegląd Statystyczny (Statistical Review)*, No. 3/4, 1958.

the whole time series on the graph the time curve will also display a linear tendency.

The above model of a random process dependent upon time enables us to formulate the following definition:

Definition 1. Function $\psi(t)$ is a trend I of the random variable X_t depending upon time (see also [15], [27], [32]).

Every time series can, of course, be regarded as a realization of the random variable X_t corresponding to items from the hypothetical general population drawn for the sample at moments of time 1,2, ..., n.

The advantage of the above definition of trend is that it does not use any non-statistical consepts such as "law" or "tendency" but employs only notions having a definite meaning in statistics. For this reason this definition is not subject to any reservation of a formal nature.

In connection with our remarks concerning a correct definition of trend, one important problem requires explanation. Before we describe its nature let us discuss an example of a time series. Suppose that we are conducting statistical research on the dynamics of the average sugar-beet yield per hectare on individually owned peasant farms in the whole country. Every year we draw a sample from the total number of farms and on the basis of the data on sugar-beet crops obtained from this sample we calculate the average sugar-beet yield on the farms drawn for the sample. In this way we get a time series. The function $\psi(t)$ in this example is a function assigning average sugar-beet yields in *the whole country* to consecutive years.

This function is not known. We can estimate it on the basis of the data from the time series. It is not easy, however, because:

1) statistical research can be conducted only once a year—after harvests. Therefore, the flow of statistical data is very slow;

2) the function $\psi(t)$ is certainly not an expression of the functioning of some law and its graphical presentation will not be a smooth, "nice" curve. On the contrary, it can be expected that the curve will be irregular, "whimsical", will have bends and twists.

We are now going to formulate the problem mentioned before. It consists in finding a way of estimating the function $\psi(t)$ on the basis of a time series, if we know that the curve $\psi(t)$ may have a completely irregular shape. If we reject the assumption which is difficult to accept, that every time series is governed by some law, and if we define the trend as we did above, then we have to recognize that the curve can have any shape, which means that it may also depend on *the random factors*. A line determined on the basis of time series data is an estimate of the shape of the curve $\psi(t)$. The time series may be interpreted as the data from the sample taken from a population Ω_t which changes with time. When the time series is interpreted in this way we can speak not only of a trend in the population but also of a trend in the sample, which can be considered as an independent population. *The trend in the sample is*, of course, *the time series curve* $\overline{x}_1$, $\overline{x}_2$, ..., $\overline{x}_n$. Let us denote the trend in the sample by $\Lambda(t)$. When the whole population is analysed, i.e. when *the sample is identical with the population*, then $\varphi(t) = \Lambda(t)$.

The trend of the sample is an estimate of the trend of the population. Let ω_t be a sample composed of k items drawn from population Ω_t at the moment t. Because of our assumption that items for the sample are drawn and then returned, the conditions of the theorem that the sequence of arithmetic means of the sample and the arithmetic mean of the population converge stochastically, are satisfied.

On the basis of this theorem we can state that

$$P\{|x_t - \psi(t)| < \varepsilon\} \underset{k \to \infty}{\to} 1. \tag{3}$$

The above formula explains how to estimate a trend of a population by a trend of a sample. *Note that all considerations concerning random variable X_t which depends on time, apply exclusively to the interval $0 \leqslant t \leqslant m$.*

Let us now consider the situation that Ω_t contains only one item at a given moment of time $t = 1, 2, ..., n$, and the situation that the number of items in the sample is, at every moment of time, equal to the number of items in the population. In both these situations, of course, $\psi(t) \equiv \Lambda(t)$. In practice it seldom happens that the trend line is expressed by a simple, uncomplicated function. Hence, when we know from experience the values of function $\psi(t)$, and this is so in both cases mentioned, function $\psi(t)$ can be replaced by another function $\Theta(t)$ which will be represented on the graph by a smooth curve, free of the irregular breaks in the curve representing $\psi(t)$. We shall call function $\Theta(t)$ *trend II*. Let us define this term. Let $\Theta(t)$ be a function of variable t, determined for $r \leqslant t \leqslant s$ and let H_t be the statistical hypothesis that the values of the time series $x_1, x_2, ..., x_t$ at the moments of time $t \in T$ can differ at most *at random* from the corresponding values of function $\Theta(t)$.

Definition 2. The set of functions **R** determined for $t \in T$ and such that for a certain α satisfying the condition $0 < \alpha < 1$, the hypothesis H_t cannot be rejected, is called *trend II* of the time series $x_1, x_2, ..., x_t, ...$

It follows from this definition that that function for which the deviations of the time series are of a random nature is a trend II. In particular a trend II is a function represented by a broken line passing through all points (t, x_i).

Definition 2 poses the problem of the *choice* of function $\Theta(t)$. It might appear at first glance that from among the functions $\Theta(t)$ belonging to **R** we should select the function for which the sum of absolute deviations of the values of the time series from the values of $\Theta(t)$ is a minimum. However, this is not so.

The minimum sum of absolute deviations will belong to the broken line *passing through* all points $(1,x_1)$, $(2,x_2)$, ..., (t,x_t),.... This sum, of course, will equal zero. However, the following considerations are against the choice of this function. The notion of the trend has been introduced into the analysis of time series for two reasons:

1) because, on the assumption of a *status quo*, the trend line enables us to predict the development of phenomenon to be studied in the future;

2) because it permits us to describe functionally the development of this phenomenon in the past; this description plays an important role in all cases in which it is necessary to eliminate a tendency from the time series[1].

It follows from point 1) that the more the scientific predictions based on the trend line extend into the future, the more valuable they are in practice. From the formal point of view such predictions are an ordinary extrapolation of the trend line. Naturally, objectively justified extrapolation is possible only for *simple* functions which are represented graphically by continuous curves not having many fluctuations and breaks. If we were to extrapolate a curve having an irregular, complicated shape, we would be unable to provide a sufficiently convincing explanation for a bend or break in the extrapolated part of the curve. This leads to the necessity of selecting only the simplest functions from among those belonging to set **R**. There is a contradiction between these two criteria for choosing function $\Theta(t)$ from set **R**: that the shape of function $\Theta(t)$ be as simple as possible and that the sum of absolute deviations of the values of the time series

---

[1] Such a necessity is most likely to appear when the problems studied deal with stationary stochastic processes and in particular with the theory of correlation of stationary random variables.

Linear regression

from the values of function $\Theta(t)$ be as small as possible. It is the author's opinion that in selecting function $\Theta(t)$ we have first to consider the requirement that the shape of the function be as simple as possible, and then the requirement that the sum of the deviations be a minimum.

In Definition 2 it is stated that every function $\Theta(t)$ can be a trend II line if the deviations of the values of the time series from the values of the function are random. An analysis whether a function belongs to set **R** consists in the verification of hypothesis H_t. There are many tests that can be used to verify hypothesis H_t. We shall discuss here only the most useful.

6.2. Some tests for verifying hypothesis H_t

6.2.1. The run test

The run test (see 4.2.2.) can be used to verify hypothesis H_t. We shall demonstrate this by an example.

Example 1. Table 1 contains monthly operating data from the Wrocław Transport Corporation. The data cover a period of two years and are expressed in thousands of car-kilometres.

TABLE 1

CAR–KILOMETRES OPERATED IN WROCŁAW

No	Car-km thous.	No	Car-km thous.	No	Car-km thous.	No	Car-km thous.
1	1,163	7	1,201	13	1,326	19	1,498
2	1,034	8	1,215	14	1,221	20	1,504
3	1,094	9	1,191	15	1,372	21	1,479
4	1,080	10	1,242	16	1,302	22	1,576
5	1,210	11	1,213	17	1,401	23	1,598
6	1,127	12	1,252	18	1,495	24	1,617
			14,022				17,389

The time curve based on these data is shown on Graph 1. This curve displays a clearly marked growth tendency.

GRAPH 1.

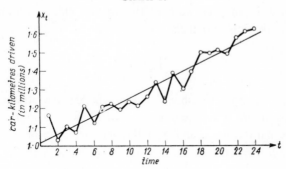

A linear function has been used to express this tendency

$$\tilde{x} = at + b,$$

in which

$$a = \frac{\overline{x}_{(2)} - \overline{x}_{(1)}}{\overline{t}_{(2)} - \overline{t}_{(1)}}, \qquad (1)$$

where

$$\overline{x}_{(1)} = \frac{1}{l} \sum_{1}^{l} x_t, \qquad 1 \leqslant l < n,$$

$$\overline{x}_{(2)} = \frac{1}{n-l} \sum_{l+1}^{n} x_t,$$

$$\overline{t}_{(1)} = \frac{1}{l} \sum_{1}^{l} t,$$

$$\overline{t}_{(2)} = \frac{1}{n-l} \sum_{l+1}^{n} t,$$

and

$$b = \overline{x} - a\overline{t}, \qquad (2)$$

whereas

$$\overline{x} = \frac{1}{n} \sum_1^n x_t, \qquad \overline{t} = \frac{1}{n} \sum_1^n t.$$

When n is an even number (in practice this condition can always be satisfied) then

$$a = \frac{4}{n^2} \left(\sum_1^{n/2} x_t - \sum_{n/2+1}^n x_t \right). \tag{3}$$

In our example we should check whether the straight line expressed by the equation $x = at + b$ is a trend II line.

The parameters a and b of this line are determined by (2) and (3). We have

$$a = \frac{4}{24^2} (17{,}389 - 14{,}022) = \frac{3{,}367}{144} = 23 \cdot 4,$$

$$\overline{t} = 12 \cdot 5, \qquad \overline{x} = \frac{14{,}022 + 17{,}389}{24} = 1{,}309,$$

$$b = 1{,}309 - 23 \cdot 4 \cdot 12 \cdot 5 = 1{,}017.$$

We would like to draw the reader's attention to the simplicity of the computations involved in the determination of parameters a and b by formulae (2) and (3).

These computations are much simpler than those required for the method of least squares. The method of determining the parameters of the trend line proposed by the author is a special case of the determination of the regression parameters by the two-point method[1].

Let us denote by A an event in which the point with coordinates (t, x_t) is located above the trend line $\tilde{x} = at + b$, and by B an event in which such a point is located below the trend

---

[1] The usefulness of this method for determining trends was indicated to the author by J. Oderfeld.

line. *We do not take into account* the points located *exactly* on the trend line. In practice the last situation has no chance of occurring since its probability is zero. As we can see from the calculations and from Graph 1 in our example, the following sequence of events occurred

$$ABABABAABBBBABABBAAABAAA.$$

The maximum length of run in this sequence is $k = 4$. It follows from Table 1, 4.2.1., that for $n = 24$ the value of k required to reject hypothesis H_t at the level of significance $a = 0.05$ would have to be at least 8. This means that there are no grounds for rejecting the hypothesis that the values of the time series deviate from the line $\tilde{x} = 23.4\,t + 1,017$ only at random. In accordance with definition 2 the line with this equation is a *trend II* line of the time series under consideration.

6.2.2. The χ^2 test

The χ^2 test can be used to verify hypothesis H_t. Let us assume that if the deviations of the values of the time series from the line $x = at + b$ are random, then the probability of a positive deviation equals the probability of a negative deviation, so

$$P(A) = P(B) = 1/2.$$

Let us denote by r the number of events A. In this case, for a sufficiently large sample, the distribution of the random variable

$$\frac{2\left(r - \dfrac{n}{2}\right)^2}{n} + \frac{2\left(n - r - \dfrac{n}{2}\right)^2}{n} = \frac{(2r - n)^2}{n} \qquad (1)$$

approximates the χ^2 distribution with one degree of freedom.

6.2.3. Pitman's test

*

Both tests described above are very simple to use. Their drawback is that they react only to the *sign of the deviations* of the values of the time series from the trend line and not to the *magnitude of these deviations*. Pitman's test is free of this drawback. We shall now discuss this test (see [33], p. 128–131).

Suppose that we have two samples ω_1, and ω_2 with frequencies m and r respectively. In sample ω_1, the sequence of values y_1, y_2, ... y_m has been obtained, and in sample ω_2 the sequence of values z_1, z_2, ... z_r. Let us define

$$\bar{y} = \frac{1}{m} \sum_{i=1}^{m} y_i \,,$$

$$\bar{z} = \frac{1}{r} \sum_{j=1}^{r} z_j \,, \tag{1}$$

$$\bar{v} = \frac{1}{m+r} \left(\sum_{i=1}^{m} y_i + \sum_{j=1}^{r} z_j \right).$$

The number of combinations of $m+r$ items taken m at a time equals $N = C_{m+r}^{m}$. This is the number of ways a set of $m+r$ items can be divided into two subgroups numbering m and r items respectively. Samples ω_1 and ω_2 form one such division into subgroups of m and r items.

Let us denote by M the number of such divisions which have a certain property W distinguishing them from the remaining $N-M$ divisions. In this case the probability of the occurrence of a division with property W is equal to the fraction M/N. Let us introduce the quantity

$$R = |\bar{y} - \bar{z}|, \tag{2}$$

which we shall call the range of the division, or briefly —

the range. Let property W consist of $R \geqslant R_0$ where R_0 is a certain positive number. Let us select R_0 so that

$$M/N \leqslant a, \text{ i.e. } M \leqslant Na, \tag{3}$$

where a is a real number satisfying the condition $0 < a < 1$. We shall consider that samples ω_1 and ω_2 come from the same population, i.e. that *they can differ from one another only at random* if the corresponding range $R < R_0$. Otherwise we shall assume that ω_1 and ω_2 come from two different populations.

Let us denote by y_i $(i = 1, 2, ..., m)$ the positive deviations of the values of the series from the probable trend line, i.e.

$$y_i = [x_t - \Theta(t)] > 0, \tag{4}$$

and by $-z_j$ $(j = 1, 2, ..., r)$ the negative deviations of this series, i.e.

$$-z_j = [x_t - \Theta(t)] < 0. \tag{5}$$

The computations connected with the verification of hypothesis H_t by Pitman's test will be explained on a numerical example.

Example 1. The average employment in Poland in 1949–1955 was as follows (see [65], p. 277)

Years	1949	1950	1951	1952	1953	1954	1955
Employment in tens of thousands	43·5	51·6	56·3	58·9	62·7	65·2	67·6

Assuming $a = 0.05$ check whether the line $x_t = 3 \cdot 5t + 44$ may be considered a trend II line.

The deviations of the time series from a line with this equation are given in Table 1.

TABLE 1

EMPLOYMENT IN POLAND 1949–1955

x_t	$\tilde{x}_t$	y	z
43·5	47·5		4·0
51·6	51·0	0·6	
56·3	54·5	1·8	
58·9	58·0	0·9	
62·7	61·5	1·2	
65·2	65·0	0·2	
67·6	68·5		0·9

The total number of the combinations in our example equals

$$N = C_7^2 = 21 .$$

Hence

$$M \leqslant 0·05 . 21 = 1·05, \text{ i.e. } M = 1 .$$

To arrange the combinations according to declining values of R we shall use the formula

$$r \, |\bar{z} - \bar{v}| = |\Sigma z - r\bar{v}| . \tag{6}$$

In our example $r = 2$, $\Sigma z = 4·9$, $\bar{v} = 1·39$. In this case

$$r \, |\bar{z} - \bar{v}| = |\, 4·9 - 2·78 \,| = 2·12 .$$

Here are 3 out of 21 combinations for which the corresponding pairs of numbers inserted into formula (6) give a value not less than 2·12:

$$4·0 \quad 1·8$$
$$4·0 \quad 0·9$$
$$4·0 \quad 0·9.$$

Since to reject hypothesis H_t the number of combinations may not be greater than $M = 1$, in our example there are no grounds for rejecting hypothesis H_t.

Pitman's test is awkward to use because of the necessity of finding combinations with property W. The computations become cumbersome when the total number of combinations N is large. In such cases, however, we can use the random variable

$$\sqrt{\frac{wk}{1-w}}, \qquad (7)$$

which has a distribution similar to Student's distribution with the number of degrees of freedom given by:

$$k = m + r - 2,$$

where w is expressed by the equation

$$w = \frac{m}{r} \cdot \frac{(\bar{y} - \bar{v})^2}{s^2} \qquad (8)$$

in which s denotes the standard deviation calculated on the basis of the data from both samples ω_1 and ω_2.

6.3. The determination of trend ex post and ex ante

Let us consider two examples, taken from real life, in which it is necessary to determine trends.

Example 1. It is desired to study the relationship, in a certain enterprise, between the amount of production outlay Y and the volume of production X. The purpose of this research is to find the regression equation of Y on X. The knowledge of this equation is of great practical importance since it enables us to assign to a given volume of production the expected size of outlay. The question arises, however, whether production and outlay, or at least one of these quantities, are not correlated with time since the efforts of the employees are constantly concentrated on increasing production and lowering costs, thus creating a regular factor which would explain such a correlation of variables X and Y with time. To answer this question we have to check whether variables X and Y show a time *tendency*. There are no difficulties as far as variable X, i.e. production, is concerned. The situation is more difficult with respect to variable Y, i.e. outlay which may be correlated not only with time, but also with variable X. *If variable Y is correlated with time* then instead of the regression line equation we have to calculate the regression line surface. When any of the variables *shows a time tendency*, then we always have to remember that it is not advisable to use the same regression equation for two periods which are far apart. As we can see, an analysis of tendencies plays an important part in proper research on the relationship between outlay and production.

Example 2. The workers in a mine have reported that they have extracted more coal than in the preceding month. They consider that this is an achievement deserving notice. It seems, however, that only those production effects can be regarded as achievements that *are of a permanent nature*. The workers of a mine can claim a worth-while achievement in increasing production only *when the production trend is an increasing function of time*. There is hardly any economic advantage to increasing production in one month in comparison with the preceding month if it drops considerably in the following month. Such fluctuations in production may be caused by random factors and they cannot constitute a basis for an appraisal or an economic decision.

In the two examples given above the trend line was needed to appraise *ex post* the phenomenon studied. The conclusions reached on the basis of the trend line *pertain to the past*.

Below is the procedure connected with the determination of the trend line needed for the analysis of a given phenomenon in the past:

1) the accumulation of statistical data for the period to be studied;
2) the preparation of a time graph on the basis of accumulated statistical data;

3) the determination — by appropriate methods — of the equation of the line which is to express the tendency of the time curve;

4) the verification whether this line can be considered a trend line.

If the determination of the trend line follows the order mentioned above then we shall regard this line *as determined ex post*.

The situation is different when the trend line is determined currently as the statistical data become available, and when the trend appears *before* the statistical analysis is finished, and when it is used not so much for the appraisal of a given phenomenon in *the past* as for predicting its behaviour *in the future*. In this case the procedure involved in the determination of the trend is as follows:

1) the selection of the significance coefficient α;

2) the determination of the minimum value of n which enables us to reject hypothesis H_t at the level α (note: when the two-point method is used for the determination of the parameters of the trend, then n has to be an even number). If we verify hypothesis H_t by a run test, $n = 10$, when $\alpha = 0.05$ (see Table 1, 4.2.2.);

3) on the basis of $n - 1$ consecutive points of the time curve[1] the equation of the straight line $x = a_1t + b_1$ is determined and the hypothesis $H_t^{(1)}$ formulated that in the interval $[1,n]$ the equation of the trend line is $\tilde{x}_t^{(1)} = a_1t + b_1$. If the hypothesis is not rejected we formulate the hypothesis $H_t^{(2)}$ that this equation will be a trend line equation in the interval $[1,n+1]$. We continue this procedure until there appear grounds for rejecting hypothesis $H_t^{(r)}$ where r is the number of the hypothesis at the time of rejecting it;

---

[1] or $n-2$ when the two-point method is used.

4) after rejecting hypothesis $H_t^{(r)}$ the new line $\tilde{x}_t^{(r)} = a_r t + b_r$ is determined on the basis of $n-1$ *last points* of the time curve and *a new* hypothesis is formulated; it is considered that since none of the remaining points provides grounds for rejecting hypothesis $H_t^{(r-1)}$ then the equation $\tilde{x}_t^{(r-1)} = a_{r-1} t + b_{r-1}$ is the equation of trend II of these points. The procedure is then repeated according to the instructions in points 3 and 4.

This procedure *prevents us from recognizing as a trend line a curve which does not satisfy the condition of random deviations* formulated in Definition 2. On the other hand this procedure enables us to determine the trend line *currently*, without waiting until "the law governing the time series" emerges.

The trend line obtained in this way we shall call the *ex ante line* since it is determined *before* the statistical analysis is finished. The procedure involved in the determination of the *ex ante* line is a sequential procedure.

The *ex ante* trend line is composed of different straight line segments following each other, and the equation of this line is written as a sequence of linear functions corresponding to these straight lines.

This is a little troublesome, but it should be remembered that after the accumulation of sufficient statistical data, the *ex ante* trend line can always be replaced by the *ex post* trend line.

Example 3. Table 1 contains the data on the monthly production of automobiles in the United States in 1905–1928.

The time curve based on the data from Table 1 is shown on Graph 1. It is a broken line shown as a thick line on the Graph. The thin broken line composed of two segments is a trend II line determined by the *sequential* procedure. The equation of the first segment of the trend line is $\tilde{x}_t = 3{\cdot}8t - 5$. The straight line of this equation is a trend line for 1905–1912. The trend for the following years is the line $\tilde{x}_t = 22{\cdot}5t - 168$.

TABLE 1

MONTHLY AUTOMOBILE PRODUCTION
IN THE USA 1905–1928

t	Years	x_t in thous./month
1	1905	2·1
2	1906	2·8
3	1907	3·7
4	1908	5·4
5	1909	10·9
6	1910	15·6
7	1911	17·5
8	1912	31·5
9	1913	40·4
10	1914	47·4
11	1915	80·8
12	1916	134·8
13	1917	156·2
14	1918	97·6
15	1919	161·1
16	1920	185·6
17	1921	134·7
18	1922	212·0
19	1923	336·2
20	1924	300·2
21	1925	355·5
22	1926	358·4
23	1927	283·4
24	1928	363·2

(see [35], pp. 193–194).

The dotted line shown on Graph 1 is the *ex post* trend line.
It is a logistic curve with the equation

$$\tilde{x}_t = \frac{320\cdot83}{1 + e^{1\cdot4925} \cdot e^{-0\cdot1569\,t}}.$$

To determine the equation of this curve the data for 1903–
1941 were used. The statistical data for 1929–1941 are not

14

shown in Table 1 because the author believes that the deviations from the trend line can only be of a random nature. Two events which took place in the period 1929–1941 have made it impossible to analyse the majority of economic phenomena by trend methods. These events were the economic crisis and war.

GRAPH 1.

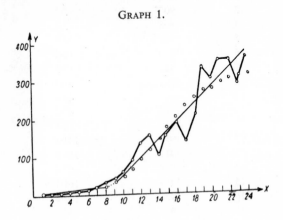

As can be seen from Graph 1, the broken line with the equation

$$\tilde{x}_t = \begin{cases} 3{\cdot}8t - 5 & 1 \leqslant t \leqslant 8, \\ 22{\cdot}5t - 168 & 9 \leqslant t \leqslant 24, \end{cases} \tag{1}$$

and the continuous line with the equation

$$\tilde{x}_t = \frac{320{\cdot}83}{1 + e^{1{\cdot}4925} \cdot e^{-0{\cdot}1569t}} \qquad 1 \leqslant t \leqslant 24 \tag{2}$$

have approximately the same shape. Both lines can be regarded as trend II lines because, according to Definition 2 in 6.1., these lines are equivalent since they belong to set **R**. This does not mean that it is a matter of indifference which of these lines should be considered as more useful in practical

applications. The great advantage of line (1) is the simplicity
of the computations involved in the determination of its parameters and the lack of any indication that there exists a law
governing the stochastic process under consideration. Its
drawback is that it is a broken line composed of straight line
segments. The advantage of the line with equation (2) is that
it is a continuous line without breaks and can be expressed
analytically as one function. Its disadvantages are the more
difficult computations involved in the determination of the
parameters of its equation and a temptation to interpret the
equation of the line as a law expressed in mathematical
language, governing the development in time of the phenomenon studied. According to the author, both lines can be
of service in the analysis of time series providing the notion
of the trend is properly interpreted.

The definition of the trend proposed in this work has important practical implications:

a) it introduces the concept of the set **R** of functions which
   can be considered as trend functions. In the interpretation hitherto prevailing *each* function could be a trend
   function;
b) it simplifies computations involved in the determination of the parameters of the trend line;
c) it makes possible the discovery and recognition of
   regular fluctuations (seasonal or cyclical) in the time
   series, if such fluctuations exist; they will be shown
   by a broken line determined by the sequential procedure;
d) it enables us to reduce the random variable X_t to the form
   in which this variable is not dependent upon time. This
   transformation is accomplished by the formula

$$X = X_t - \tilde{x}.$$

The determination of the trend is of great practical importance to economic research because the correct knowledge

14*

of economic processes is possible only when these processes are interpreted dynamically. Statistical methods of determining trends are part of a branch of mathematical statistics known as the theory of stochastic processes which has developed rapidly in recent years.

It is difficult to take time into account in scientific research and it is not surprising that the more important achievements of statistics in this field are only a matter of recent years. As we know, correlation analysis is one of the main research tools used in the theory of stochastic processes. Thus new and broad fields for applications are opening up before the correlation and regression methods. This leads us to believe that correlation and regression theory will be studied with interest and, in consequence, will be further developed.

APPENDIX

PROOFS OF THEOREMS AND STATISTICAL DATA USED IN THE BOOK

Proof of Theorem 1 from 3.3.1.

The proof can be written as follows:

$$\begin{vmatrix} \bar{x}_{(1)} - \bar{x}, & \bar{y}_{(1)} - \bar{y} \\ \bar{x}_{(2)} - \bar{x}, & \bar{y}_{(2)} - \bar{y} \end{vmatrix} = 0.$$

To prove the theorem we have to show that:

$$(\bar{y}_{(2)} - \bar{y})(\bar{x}_{(1)} - \bar{x}) = (\bar{y}_{(1)} - \bar{y})(\bar{x}_{(2)} - \bar{x}).$$

In the proof we shall use the following
Lemma 1.

$$\frac{\bar{x}_{(2)} - \bar{x}}{\bar{x} - \bar{x}_{(1)}} = \frac{n - k}{k}.$$

Proof of the Lemma:

$$\frac{\bar{x}_{(2)} - \bar{x}}{\bar{x} - \bar{x}_{(1)}} = \frac{\dfrac{1}{k} \sum x_{(2)} - \dfrac{1}{n} \sum x}{\dfrac{1}{n} \sum x - \dfrac{1}{n-k} \sum x_{(1)}}$$

$$= \frac{(n-k)\left[n \sum x_{(2)} - k \sum x\right]}{k\left[(n-k) \sum x - n \sum x_{(1)}\right]}$$

$$= \frac{(n-k)\left[n \sum x_{(2)} - k \sum x\right]}{k\left[n \sum x_{(1)} + n \sum x_{(2)} - k \sum x - n \sum x_{(1)}\right]}$$

$$= \frac{n - k}{k}.$$

Similarly we can prove
Lemma 2.

$$\frac{\overline{y}_{\langle 2\rangle} - \overline{y}}{\overline{y}_{\langle 1\rangle} - \overline{y}} = \frac{n-k}{k}.$$

The correctness of the theorem follows directly from Lemmas 1 and 2.

Note: a similar proof can be given for the more general theorem that points $(\overline{x}_{(1)}\overline{y}_{\langle 1\rangle})$, $(\overline{x}_{(2)}, \overline{y}_{\langle 2\rangle})$, $(\overline{x}, \overline{y})$ are located on the same straight line. In this theorem the set ω is arbitrarily divided into two subgroups, e.g. by means of the number x, satisfying the inequality

$$x_{min} \leqslant x_1 \leqslant x_{max}$$

where x_{min} denotes the smallest abscissa and x_{max} the greatest abscissa of the points belonging to ω.

COMPUTATION TABLE FOR EXAMPLE 1 FROM 4.1.2.

No	x	y	$x-w$ +	$x-w$ −	$y-u$ +	$y-u$ −	$(x-w)^2$	$(y-u)^2$	$(x-w)(y-u)$ +	$(x-w)(y-u)$ −
1	183	175		7		5	49	25	35	
2	184	172		6		8	36	64	48	
3	180	168		10		12	100	144	120	
4	164	156		26		24	676	576	624	
5	177	190		13	10		169	100		130
6	159	160		31		20	961	400	620	
7	147	142		43		38	1,849	1,444	1,634	
8	151	153		39		27	1,521	729	1,053	
9	164	149		26		31	676	961	806	
10	122	128		68		52	4,624	2,706	3,536	
11	167	167		23		13	529	169	299	
12	188	172		2		8	4	64	16	
13	180	162		10		18	100	324	180	
14	156	160		34		20	1,156	400	680	
15	163	154		27		26	729	676	702	
16	175	160		15		20	225	400	300	
17	173	179		17		1	289	1	17	
18	158	144		32		36	1,024	1,296	1,152	
19	190	193	0	0	13		0	169	0	0
20	180	169		10		11	100	121	110	
21	196	177	6			3	36	9		18
22	206	190	16		10		256	100	160	
23	199	186	9		6		81	36	54	
24	201	180	11		0		121	0	0	0
25	207	182	17		2		289	4	34	
26	209	190	19		10		361	100	190	
27	184	164		6		16	36	256	96	
28	165	164		25		16	625	256	400	
29	142	149		48		31	2,304	961	1,488	
30	116	133		74		47	5,476	2,209	3,478	
31	147	164		43		16	1,849	256	688	
32	175	168		15		12	225	144	180	
33	197	176	7			4	49	16		28
34	202	186	12		6		144	36	72	
35	189	183		1	3		1	9		3
36	190	176	0	0		4	0	16	0	0
37	180	191		10	11		100	121		110

No	x	y	$x-w$ +	$x-w$ −	$y-u$ +	$y-u$ −	$(x-w)^2$	$(y-u)^2$	$(x-w)(y-u)$ +	$(x-w)(y-u)$ −
38	170	167		20		13	400	169	260	
39	182	161		8		19	64	361	152	
40	189	180		1	0	0	1	0	0	0
41	213	191	23		11		529	121	253	
42	301	264	111		84		12,321	7,056	9,324	
43	225	202	35		22		1,225	484	770	
44	234	214	44		34		1,936	1,156	1,496	
45	203	184	13		4		169	16	52	
46	192	189	2		9		4	81	18	
47	191	179	1			1	1	1		1
48	146	155		44		25	1,936	625	1,100	
49	193	173	3			7	9	49		21
50	187	166		3		14	9	196	42	
51	187	182		3	2		9	4		6
52	212	205	22		25		484	625	550	
53	251	216	61		36		3,721	1,296	2,196	
54	220	201	30		21		900	441	630	
55	180	164		10		16	100	256	160	
56	207	191	17		11		289	121	187	
57	190	173	0	0		7	0	49	0	0
58	185	174		5		6	25	36	30	
59	186	170		4		10	16	100	40	
60	181	166		9		14	81	196	126	
61	192	179	2			1	4	1		2
62	203	191	13		11		169	121	143	
63	277	247	87		67		7,569	4,489	5,829	
64	299	257	109		77		11,881	5,929	8,393	
65	215	206	25		26		625	676	650	
66	200	188	10		8		100	64	80	
67	192	167	2			13	4	169		26
68	187	183		3	3		9	9		9
69	194	190	4		10		16	100	40	
70	194	182	4		2		16	4	8	
71	190	178	0	0		2	0	4	0	0
72	278	241	88		61		7,744	3,721	5,368	
Σ	13,712	12,888	803	771	595	667	79,136	44,024	56,669	354

$\bar{x} = 190{\cdot}4, \quad \bar{y} = 179, \quad w = 190, \quad u = 180.$

COMPUTATION TABLE FOR EXAMPLE 1 FROM 4.2.2.

No	x	y	$x-u$ +	$x-u$ −	$y-w$ +	$y-w$ −	$(x-u)^2$	$(y-w)^2$	$(x-u)(y-w)$ +	$(x-u)(y-w)$ −
1	12	27		108		13	11,664	169	1,404	
2	56	25		64		15	4,096	225	960	
3	65	31		55		9	3,025	81	495	
4	114	34		6		6	36	36	36	
5	137	38	17			2	289	4		34
6	110	39		10		1	100	1	10	
7	129	42	9		2		81	4	18	
8	141	46	21		5		441	25	105	
9	133	45	13		5		169	25	65	
10	94	38		26		2	676	4	52	
11	73	34		47		6	2,209	36	282	
12	85	34		35		6	1,225	36	210	
13	131	41	11		1		121	1	11	
14	145	41	25		1		625	1	25	
15	195	47	75		7		5,625	49	525	
16	200	47	80		7		6,400	49	560	
17	193	58	73		18		5,329	324	1,314	
18	197	53	77		13		5,929	169	1,001	
19	136	48	16		8		256	64	128	
20	104	46		16	6		256	36		96
21	88	41		32	1		1,024	1		32
22	107	41		13	1		169	1		13
Σ	2,645	896	417	412	75	60	49,745	1,341	7,201	175

$\bar{x} = 120 \cdot 2, \quad \bar{y} = 40 \cdot 7,$

$u = 120, \quad w = 40,$

$\sum (x-\bar{x})(y-\bar{y}) \approx 7{,}026,$

$\sum (x-\bar{x})^2 \approx 49{,}745,$

$\sum (y-\bar{y})^2 \approx 1{,}341,$

$a_{21} = 0 \cdot 141, \quad b_{21} = 23 \cdot 8.$

COMPUTATION TABLE FOR EXAMPLE 1 FROM 4.3.

No	x	y	$x_{(2)}$	$y_{(2)}$
1	267	141		
2	254	159		
3	249	112		
4	344	152	344	152
5	246	119		
6	411	207	411	207
7	217	114		
8	219	118		
9	359	152	359	152
10	378	150	378	150
11	256	135	256	135
12	406	160	406	160
13	258	117		
14	213	84		
15	345	129	345	129
16	273	164		
17	251	76		
18	225	126		
19	254	149		
20	194	113		
$\sum$	5,619	2,677	2,499	1,085

$\bar{x} = 280 \cdot 95, \quad \bar{y} = 133 \cdot 85, \quad \bar{x}_{(2)} = 357, \quad \bar{y}_{(2)} = 155.$

$a_{21} = \dfrac{155 - 134}{357 - 281} = \dfrac{21}{76} \approx 0 \cdot 28,$

$b_{21} = 133 \cdot 85 - 0 \cdot 28 \cdot 280 \cdot 95 \approx 55.$

COMPUTATIONS FOR EXAMPLE 1 FROM 4.3.

$$a_{21} = \frac{26,447}{85,373} \approx 0.31, \text{ (see Table 2, item 3.2.2.),}$$

$$b_{21} = 133.85 - 0.31,280.95 \approx 47,$$

$$s_{21} = \sqrt{\frac{16,757 - 0.31.26,447}{20}} = \sqrt{428} \approx 20.69,$$

$$s_1^2 = \frac{85,373}{20} = 4,269, \qquad s_1 = \sqrt{4,269} \approx 65.$$

$x - \bar{x}$	$(x-\bar{x})^2$	$(x-\bar{x})^2 + 4269$	$\dfrac{(x-\bar{x})^2 + 4269}{18.4269}$	$\sqrt{\dfrac{(x-\bar{x})^2 + 4269}{18.4269}}$	$20{\cdot}69.\sqrt{\dfrac{(x-\bar{x})^2 + 4269}{18.4269}}$	$2{\cdot}55.20{\cdot}69.\sqrt{\dfrac{(x-\bar{x})^2 + 4269}{18.4269}}$
−81	6,561	10,830	0.1409	0.38	7.9	20.1
−61	3,721	7,990	0.1040	0.32	6.6	16.8
−41	1,681	5,950	0.0774	0.28	5.8	14.8
−21	441	4,710	0.0613	0.25	5.2	13.3
−1	1	4,170	0.0543	0.23	4.8	12.2
19	361	4,630	0.0603	0.25	5.2	13.3
39	1,521	5,790	0.0754	0.28	5.8	14.8
59	3,481	7,750	0.1009	0.32	6.6	16.8
79	6,241	10,510	0.1368	0.37	7.7	19.6
99	9,801	14,070	0.1831	0.43	8.9	22.7
119	14,161	18,430	0.2398	0.49	10.1	25.8
139	19,321	23,590	0.3070	0.55	11.4	29.1

COMPUTATION TABLE FOR EXAMPLE 2 FROM 4.3.

No	x	y	$x-u$ +	$x-u$ −	$y-w$ +	$y-w$ −	$(x-u)^2$	$(y-w)^2$	$(x-u)(y-w)$ +	$(x-u)(y-w)$ −
1	12	292		108		158	11,664	24,964	17,064	
2	56	308		64		142	4,096	20,164	9,088	
3	65	388		55		62	3,025	3,844	3,410	
4	114	388		6		62	36	3,844	372	
5	137	517	17		67		289	4,489	1,139	
6	110	545		10	95		100	9,025		950
7	129	536	9		86		81	7,396	774	
8	141	536	21		86		441	7,396	1,806	
9	133	561	13		111		169	12,321	1,443	
10	95	512		25	62		625	3,844		1,550
11	73	459		47	9		2,209	81		423
12	62	446		58		4	3,364	16	232	
$\sum_1^{12}$	1,127	5,488	60	373	516	428	26,099	97,384	35,328	2,923
13	195	414	75			36	5,625	1,296		2,700
14	200	463	80		13		6,400	169	1,040	
15	193	448	73			2	5,329	4		146
16	197	449	77			1	5,929	1		77
17	136	435	16			15	256	225		240
18	104	373		16		77	256	5,929	1,232	
19	88	361		32		89	1,024	7,921	2,848	
20	107	366		13		84	169	7,056	1,092	
$\sum_{12}^{20}$	1,220	3,309	321	61	13	304	24,988	22,601	6,212	3,163
$\sum_1^{20}$	2,347	8,797	381	434	529	732	51,087	119,985	41,540	6,086

The determination of the parameters of line I.

$$\bar{x} = 117 \cdot 4, \qquad \bar{y} = 439 \cdot 9,$$

$$u = 120, \qquad w = 450,$$

$$\Delta_u = -2 \cdot 6, \qquad \Delta_w = -10 \cdot 1,$$

$$\sum_{1}^{20} (x - \bar{x})(y - \bar{y}) = 35{,}454 - 20(-2 \cdot 6)(-10 \cdot 1) = 34{,}929,$$

$$\sum_{1}^{20} (x - \bar{x})^2 = 51{,}087 - 20(-2 \cdot 6)^2 = 50{,}952,$$

$$a_{21} = \frac{34{,}929}{50{,}952} = 0 \cdot 69,$$

$$b_{21} = 439 \cdot 9 - 0 \cdot 69 \, . \, 117 \cdot 4 = 359.$$

The determination of the parameters of line II.

$$\bar{x} = 93 \cdot 9, \qquad \bar{y} = 457 \cdot 3,$$

$$u = 120, \qquad w = 450,$$

$$\Delta_u = -26 \cdot 1, \qquad \Delta_w = 7 \cdot 3,$$

$$\sum_{1}^{12} (x - \bar{x})(y - \bar{y}) = 32{,}405 - 12(-26 \cdot 1)(7 \cdot 3) = 34{,}691,$$

$$\sum_{1}^{12} (x - \bar{x})^2 = 26{,}099 - 12(-26 \cdot 1)^2 = 17{,}953,$$

$$a_{21} = \frac{34{,}691}{17{,}953} = 1 \cdot 93,$$

$$b_{21} = 457 \cdot 3 - 1 \cdot 93 \, . \, 93 \cdot 9 = 276 \cdot 5.$$

The determination of the parameters of line III.

$$\bar{x} = 152 \cdot 5, \qquad \bar{y} = 414,$$

$$u = 120, \qquad w = 450,$$

$$\Delta_u = 32 \cdot 5, \qquad \Delta_w = -36,$$

$$\sum_{12}^{20} (x - \bar{x})(y - \bar{y}) = 3{,}049 - 8(32 \cdot 5)(-36) = 12{,}409,$$

$$\sum_{12}^{20} (x - \bar{x})^2 = 24{,}988 - 8(32 \cdot 5)^2 = 16{,}538,$$

$$a_{21} = \frac{12{,}409}{16{,}538} = 0 \cdot 75,$$

$$b_{21} = 414 - 0 \cdot 75 \cdot 152 \cdot 5 = 300.$$

LIST OF SYMBOLS

* Page on which the symbol was used for the first time.

Symbol	The meaning of the symbol	Page
Δ	increase in consumption	69
e_{yi}	the i-th residual	32
E_1	energy produced	79
E_2	energy used up	79
ε	non-negative constant	138
e	the relative efficiency of the regression coefficient obtained by the two-point method	139
$f(x,y)$	the density function of a two-dimensional random variable	18
$f_1(x)$	marginal density	18
$F(x,y)$	two-dimensional distribution function	17
$f(y\|x)$	the conditional density function	20
$\varphi(x,y)$	the density of the two-dimensional normal distribution	43
γ	rotation angle in a sample	149
$g_1(x)$	regression of Y on X	25
$g_2(y)$	regression of X on Y	25
H_L	hypothesis that the regression line in the population is a straight line	159
H_t	hypothesis that the line belongs to set **R**	196
H_r	hypothesis that the regression lines obtained by the classical method and the two-point method do not differ significantly	171
h	class interval of Y	116
η_y η_x $\Big\}$	correlation ratios	37
η	the coefficient of efficiency	79
k	the number of classes in the frequency distribution of X	115
k	the number of points with abscissa greater than $\bar{x}$	125
l	the number of classes in the frequency distribution of Y	115
λ	the slope of the orthogonal regression line in a population	42
m_1	$E(X)$	43
m_2	$E(Y)$	43

Symbol	The meaning of the symbol	Page
m_{lk}	$E(X^l Y^k)$	21
m_{10}	$E(X)$	22
m_{01}	$E(Y)$	22
m_{11}	$E(XY)$	22
m_{20}	$E(X^2)$	22
m_{02}	$E(Y^2)$	22
μ_{lk}	$E[(X-m_{10})^l(Y-m_{01})^k]$	22
μ_{10}	$E[(X-m_{10})^1 (Y-m_{01})^0] = 0$	22
μ_{01}	$E[(X-m_{10})^0 (Y-m_{01})^1] = 0$	22
μ_{20}	$V(X)$	23
μ_{02}	$V(Y)$	23
μ_{11}	$C(XY)$	23
m	the number of points with abscissa greater than $\bar{y}$	127
n_{ij}	frequency in the contingency table	115
n	the number of variables	12
n	the size of the sample	100
N	population	69
$N(0,1)$	normal distribution with parameters $m = 0$, $\sigma = 1$	139
Ω	general population	100
ω	sample	100
Θ	the rotation angle of a population	42
p_{ij}	probability that $X=x_i$ and $Y=y_i$	13
$p_{\cdot j}$	marginal probability	14
$p_{i\cdot}$	,, ,,	14
$p(y_j\|x_i)$	conditional probability	15
$p(x_i\|y_j)$	,, ,,	15
Q_i	the i-th need	56
P	price	71
R_2	two-dimensional space	13
ϱ	the correlation coefficient in a population	38
r	,, ,, ,, ,, ,, sample	103
σ_{21}	the standard error of estimation in a population	33
σ_{12}	,, ,, ,, ,, ,, ,, ,, ,,	33
σ_1	the standard deviation in a population	43
σ_2	,, ,, ,, ,, ,, ,,	43

Symbol	The meaning of the symbol	Page
S_{21}	the standard error of estimation in a sample (random variable)	167
s_{21}	the standard error of estimation in a sample (realization of random variable)	102
s_{12}	the standard error of estimation in a sample (realization of random variable)	102
s_1	the standard deviation in a sample (realization of random variable)	102
S_1	the standard deviation in a sample (random variable)	166
s_2	the standard deviation in a sample (realization of random variable)	102
S_2	the standard deviation in a sample (random variable)	166
S	the sum of financial resources	56
S''	the sum of free decisions	57
S	supply	76
t_r	$\dfrac{r - \varrho}{1 - \varrho^2} \sqrt{n - 1}$	176
t'	$\dfrac{S_1 \sqrt{n - 2}}{S_2 \sqrt{1 - r^2}} (a_{21} - \alpha_{21})$	166
t_z	$[z - E(z)] \sqrt{n - 3}$	177
t''	$\dfrac{\sqrt{n - 2}}{S_{21}} (b_{20} - \beta_{20})$	167
t	$\dfrac{\sqrt{n - 2}}{S_{21} \sqrt{1 + \dfrac{(x - \bar{x})^2}{S_1^2}}} \cdot (\tilde{y} - \hat{y})$	168
t	time	67
U	$X - m_{10}$	33
U	revenue	78
u	an arbitrary constant introduced to simplify calculations	114
$v_1(x')$	the empirical frequency distribution of variable X'	146

Symbol	The meaning of the symbol	Page
$v_2(y')$	the empirical frequency distribution of variable Y'	146
W	$Y - m_{01}$	33
W_i	the consumption of commodity A_i	72
w	an arbitrary constant introduced to facilitate calculations	114
X	production	78
X	random variable	12
$\hat{x}$	regression in a population	25
$X_{(1)}$	$X \mid X \leqslant \bar{x}$	125
$X_{(2)}$	$X \mid X > \bar{x}$	125
$X_{\langle 1 \rangle}$	$X \mid Y \leqslant \bar{y}$	127
$X_{\langle 2 \rangle}$	$X \mid Y > \bar{y}$	127
$\bar{x}_{(1)}$	$\dfrac{1}{n-k} \Sigma x_{(1)}$	125
$\bar{x}_{(2)}$	$\dfrac{1}{k} \Sigma x_{(2)}$	125
$\bar{x}_{\langle 1 \rangle}$	$\dfrac{1}{n-m} \Sigma x_{\langle 1 \rangle}$	127
$\bar{x}_{\langle 2 \rangle}$	$\dfrac{1}{m} \Sigma x_{\langle 2 \rangle}$	127
$\bar{x}$	$\dfrac{1}{n} \Sigma x_i$	101
X'	$(X - m_1) \cos \Theta + (Y - m_2) \sin \Theta$	145
$\tilde{x}$	the trend line in a sample	188
ξ	the two-dimensional random variable (X_1, X_2)	12
ξ	„ „ „ „ „ (X, Y)	12
ξ	n-dimensional random variable $(X_1, X_2, ..., X_n)$	12
Y	cost	81
Y_s	fixed cost	82
Y_z	variable cost	82
$\overline{Y}$	average cost	82
Y'	marginal cost	82
Y'	$-(X - m_1) \sin \Theta + (Y - m_2) \cos \Theta$	145
$\tilde{y}$	regression in a sample	101
$\hat{y}$	„ „ „ population	25

Symbol	The meaning of the symbol	Page
$Y_{(1)}$	$Y \mid Y \leqslant \bar{y}$	127
$Y_{(2)}$	$Y \mid Y > \bar{y}$	127
$Y_{\langle 1 \rangle}$	$Y \mid X \leqslant \bar{x}$	125
$Y_{\langle 2 \rangle}$	$Y \mid X > \bar{x}$	125
$\bar{y}_{(1)}$	$\dfrac{1}{n-m} \Sigma y_{(1)}$	127
$\bar{y}_{(2)}$	$\dfrac{1}{m} \Sigma y_{(2)}$	127
$\bar{y}_{\langle 1 \rangle}$	$\dfrac{1}{n-m} \Sigma y_{\langle 1 \rangle}$	125
$\bar{y}_{\langle 2 \rangle}$	$\dfrac{1}{m} \Sigma y_{\cdot \langle 2 \rangle}$	125
$\bar{y}$	$\dfrac{1}{n} \Sigma y_i$	101
Z	profit	78
z	$\dfrac{1}{2} \ln \dfrac{1+r}{1-r}$	177

TABLES

TABLE 1

NORMAL DISTRIBUTION

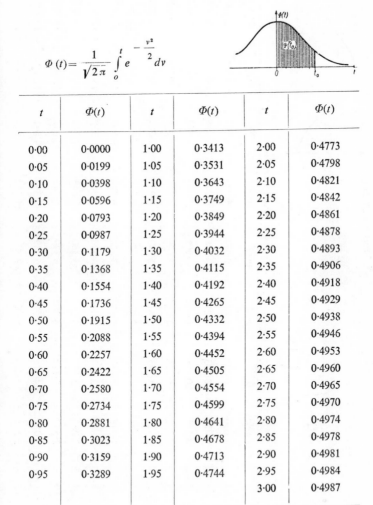

$$\Phi(t) = \frac{1}{\sqrt{2\pi}} \int_0^t e^{-\frac{v^2}{2}} dv$$

t	$\Phi(t)$	t	$\Phi(t)$	t	$\Phi(t)$
0·00	0·0000	1·00	0·3413	2·00	0·4773
0·05	0·0199	1·05	0·3531	2·05	0·4798
0·10	0·0398	1·10	0·3643	2·10	0·4821
0·15	0·0596	1·15	0·3749	2·15	0·4842
0·20	0·0793	1·20	0·3849	2·20	0·4861
0·25	0·0987	1·25	0·3944	2·25	0·4878
0·30	0·1179	1·30	0·4032	2·30	0·4893
0·35	0·1368	1·35	0·4115	2·35	0·4906
0·40	0·1554	1·40	0·4192	2·40	0·4918
0·45	0·1736	1·45	0·4265	2·45	0·4929
0·50	0·1915	1·50	0·4332	2·50	0·4938
0·55	0·2088	1·55	0·4394	2·55	0·4946
0·60	0·2257	1·60	0·4452	2·60	0·4953
0·65	0·2422	1·65	0·4505	2·65	0·4960
0·70	0·2580	1·70	0·4554	2·70	0·4965
0·75	0·2734	1·75	0·4599	2·75	0·4970
0·80	0·2881	1·80	0·4641	2·80	0·4974
0·85	0·3023	1·85	0·4678	2·85	0·4978
0·90	0·3159	1·90	0·4713	2·90	0·4981
0·95	0·3289	1·95	0·4744	2·95	0·4984
				3·00	0·4987

TABLE 2

χ^2 DISTRIBUTION

$$P\{\chi^2 > \chi_0^2\} = \int_{\chi_0^2}^{\infty} \frac{x^{\frac{k}{2}-1} e^{-\frac{x}{2}}}{\Gamma\left(\frac{k}{2}\right) 2^{\frac{k}{2}}} dx$$

χ^2 as a function k and P

k	$P = 0.99$	0.95	0.90	0.80	0.50	0.20	0.10	0.05	0.01
1	0·000	0·004	0·016	0·064	0·455	1·642	2·706	3·841	6·635
2	0·020	0·103	0·211	0·446	1·386	3·219	4·605	5·991	9·210
3	0·115	0·352	0·584	1·005	2·366	4·642	6·251	7·815	11·341
4	0·297	0·711	1·064	1·649	3·357	5·989	7·779	9·488	13·277
5	0·554	1·145	1·610	2·343	4·351	7·289	9·236	11·070	15·086
6	0·872	1·635	2·204	3·070	5·348	8·558	10·645	12·592	16·812
7	1·239	2·167	2·833	3·822	6·346	9·803	12·017	14·067	18·475
8	1·646	2·733	3·490	4·594	7·344	11·030	13·362	15·507	20·090
9	2·088	3·325	4·168	5·380	8·343	12·242	14·684	16·919	21·666
10	2·558	3·940	4·865	6·179	9·342	13·442	15·987	18·307	23·209
11	3·053	4·575	5·578	6·989	10·341	14·631	17·275	19·675	24·725
12	3·571	5·226	6·304	7·807	11·340	15·812	18·549	21·026	26·217

13	4·107	5·892	7·042	8·634	12·340	16·985	19·812	22·362	27·638
14	4·660	6·571	7·790	9·467	13·339	18·151	21·064	23·685	29·141
15	5·229	7·261	8·547	10·307	14·339	19·311	22·307	24·996	30·578
16	5·812	7·962	9·312	11·152	15·338	20·465	23·542	26·296	32·000
17	6·408	8·672	10·085	12·002	16·338	21·615	24·769	27·587	33·409
18	7·015	9·390	10·865	12·857	17·338	22·760	25·989	28·869	34·805
19	7·633	10·117	11·651	13·716	18·338	23·900	27·204	30·144	36·191
20	8·260	10·851	12·443	14·578	19·337	25·038	28·412	31·410	37·566
21	8·897	11·591	13·240	15·445	20·337	26·171	29·615	32·671	38·932
22	9·542	12·338	14·041	16·314	21·337	27·301	30·813	33·924	40·289
23	10·196	13·091	14·848	17·187	22·337	28·429	32·007	35·172	41·638
24	10·856	13·848	15·659	18·062	23·337	29·553	33·196	36·415	42·980
25	11·524	14·611	16·473	18·940	24·337	30·675	34·382	37·652	44·314
26	12·198	15·379	17·292	19·820	25·336	31·795	35·563	38·885	45·642
27	12·879	16·151	18·114	20·703	26·336	32·912	36·741	40·113	46·963
28	13·565	16·928	18·939	21·588	27·336	34·027	37·916	41·337	48·278
29	14·256	17·708	19·768	22·475	28·336	35·139	39·087	42·557	49·588
30	14·953	18·493	20·599	23·364	29·336	36·250	40·256	43·773	50·892

TABLE 3
STUDENT'S DISTRIBUTION

$$P\{|t| > t_0\} = 2 \int_{t_0}^{\infty} \frac{\Gamma\left(\frac{k+1}{2}\right)}{\Gamma\left(\frac{k}{2}\right)\sqrt{k\pi}} \left(1 + \frac{v^2}{k}\right)^{-\frac{k+1}{2}} dv$$

t as a function k and P

k	$P = 0.90$	0.80	0.70	0.50	0.30	0.20	0.10	0.02	0.01
1	0.158	0.325	0.510	1.000	1.963	3.078	6.314	31.821	63.657
2	0.142	0.289	0.445	0.816	1.386	1.886	2.920	6.965	9.925
3	0.137	0.277	0.424	0.765	1.250	1.638	2.353	4.541	5.841
4	0.134	0.271	0.414	0.741	1.190	1.533	2.132	3.747	4.604
5	0.132	0.267	0.408	0.727	1.156	1.476	2.015	3.365	4.032
6	0.131	0.265	0.404	0.718	1.134	1.440	1.943	3.143	3.707
7	0.130	0.263	0.402	0.711	1.119	1.415	1.895	2.998	3.499
8	0.130	0.262	0.399	0.706	1.108	1.397	1.860	2.896	3.355
9	0.129	0.261	0.398	0.703	1.100	1.383	1.833	2.821	3.250
10	0.129	0.260	0.397	0.700	1.093	1.372	1.812	2.764	3.169
11	0.129	0.260	0.396	0.697	1.088	1.363	1.796	2.718	3.106
12	0.128	0.259	0.395	0.695	1.083	1.356	1.782	2.681	3.055

13	0·128	0·259	0·394	0·694	1·079	1·350	1·771	2·650	3·012
14	0·128	0·258	0·393	0·692	1·076	1·345	1·761	2·624	2·977
15	0·128	0·258	0·393	0·691	1·074	1·341	1·753	2·602	2·947
16	0·128	0·258	0·392	0·690	1·071	1·337	1·746	2·583	2·921
17	0·128	0·257	0·392	0·689	1·069	1·333	1·740	2·567	2·898
18	0·127	0·257	0·392	0·688	1·067	1·330	1·734	2·552	2·878
19	0·127	0·257	0·391	0·688	1·066	1·328	1·729	2·539	2·861
20	0·127	0·257	0·391	0·687	1·064	1·325	1·725	2·528	2·845
21	0·127	0·257	0·391	0·686	1·063	1·323	1·721	2·518	2·831
22	0·127	0·256	0·390	0·686	1·061	1·321	1·717	2·508	2·819
23	0·127	0·256	0·390	0·685	1·060	1·319	1·714	2·500	2·807
24	0·127	0·256	0·390	0·685	1·059	1·318	1·711	2·492	2·797
25	0·127	0·256	0·390	0·684	1·058	1·316	1·708	2·485	2·787
26	0·127	0·256	0·390	0·684	1·058	1·315	1·706	2·479	2·779
27	0·127	0·256	0·389	0·684	1·057	1·314	1·703	2·473	2·771
28	0·127	0·256	0·389	0·683	1·056	1·313	1·701	2·467	2·763
29	0·127	0·256	0·389	0·683	1·055	1·311	1·699	2·462	2·756
30	0·127	0·256	0·389	0·683	1·055	1·310	1·697	2·457	2·750

Linear regression

TABLE 4
NORMAL DISTRIBUTION (Density function)

$$\varphi(t) = \frac{1}{\sqrt{2\pi}} e^{-\frac{t^2}{2}}$$

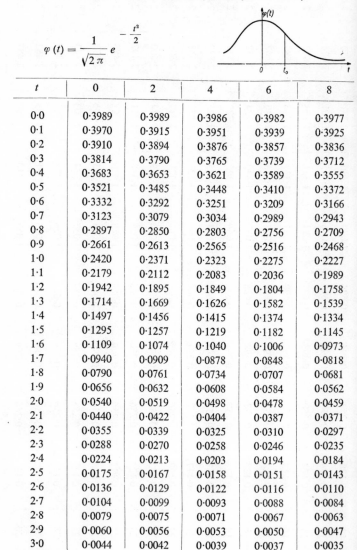

t	0	2	4	6	8
0·0	0·3989	0·3989	0·3986	0·3982	0·3977
0·1	0·3970	0·3915	0·3951	0·3939	0·3925
0·2	0·3910	0·3894	0·3876	0·3857	0·3836
0·3	0·3814	0·3790	0·3765	0·3739	0·3712
0·4	0·3683	0·3653	0·3621	0·3589	0·3555
0·5	0·3521	0·3485	0·3448	0·3410	0·3372
0·6	0·3332	0·3292	0·3251	0·3209	0·3166
0·7	0·3123	0·3079	0·3034	0·2989	0·2943
0·8	0·2897	0·2850	0·2803	0·2756	0·2709
0·9	0·2661	0·2613	0·2565	0·2516	0·2468
1·0	0·2420	0·2371	0·2323	0·2275	0·2227
1·1	0·2179	0·2112	0·2083	0·2036	0·1989
1·2	0·1942	0·1895	0·1849	0·1804	0·1758
1·3	0·1714	0·1669	0·1626	0·1582	0·1539
1·4	0·1497	0·1456	0·1415	0·1374	0·1334
1·5	0·1295	0·1257	0·1219	0·1182	0·1145
1·6	0·1109	0·1074	0·1040	0·1006	0·0973
1·7	0·0940	0·0909	0·0878	0·0848	0·0818
1·8	0·0790	0·0761	0·0734	0·0707	0·0681
1·9	0·0656	0·0632	0·0608	0·0584	0·0562
2·0	0·0540	0·0519	0·0498	0·0478	0·0459
2·1	0·0440	0·0422	0·0404	0·0387	0·0371
2·2	0·0355	0·0339	0·0325	0·0310	0·0297
2·3	0·0288	0·0270	0·0258	0·0246	0·0235
2·4	0·0224	0·0213	0·0203	0·0194	0·0184
2·5	0·0175	0·0167	0·0158	0·0151	0·0143
2·6	0·0136	0·0129	0·0122	0·0116	0·0110
2·7	0·0104	0·0099	0·0093	0·0088	0·0084
2·8	0·0079	0·0075	0·0071	0·0067	0·0063
2·9	0·0060	0·0056	0·0053	0·0050	0·0047
3·0	0·0044	0·0042	0·0039	0·0037	0·0035

BIBLIOGRAPHY

LITERATURE CITED

1. Allen, R. G. D.: *Statistics for Economists*, London, 1949.
2. Allen, R. G. D.: *Mathematical Analysis for Economists*, London, 1938.
3. Allen, R. G. D., and Bowley, A. L.: *Family Expenditure*, London, 1935.
4. Bartlett, M. S.: On the Theory of Statistical Regression, *Proc. Roy. Soc., Edinb.*, 53 (1933).
5. de Castro, J.: *Geografia głodu*, Warszawa, 1954.
6. Cournot, A.: *Recherches sur les principes mathématiques de la théorie des richesses*, Paris, 1838.
7. Cramer, H.: *Mathematical Methods of Statistics*, USA, 1946.
8. David, F. N., and Neyman, J.: Extension of the Markoff Theorem on Least Squares, *Statistical Research Memoirs*, Vol. 2 (1938).
9. Davis, L. O.: *Statistical Methods in Research and Production*, London, 1949.
10. Davis, H. T.: *The Analysis of Economic Time Series*, The Cowles Commission for Research in Economics, Monograph No. 6, Bloomington, Indiana, 1941.
11. Davis, H. T.: *Theory of Econometrics*, Bloomington, Indiana, 1941.
12. Dean, J.: Statistical Cost Functions of a Hosiery Mill, *Studies in Business Administration*, School of Business, University of Chicago, Vol. 11, No. 4, Chicago, 1941.
13. Dean, J.: *The Relation of Cost to Output for a Leather Belt Shop*, Technical Papers 2, National Bureau of Economic Research, New York, 1941.
14. Dlin, A. M.: *Matematicheskaya statistika w tekhnike*, Moscow, 1951.
15. Doob, J. L.: *Stochastic Processes*, New York, 1953.
16. Dunin-Barkowski, J. W., and Smirnow, N. W.: *Teoriya veroyatnostiej s tekhnicheskimi prilozheniami*, Moscow, 1956.
17. Ezekiel, M.: *Methods of Correlation Analysis*, New York, 1947.
18. Falewicz, J.: *Bieżąca kontrola gospodarności przedsiębiorstw przemysłowych*, Wrocław, 1949.

236 *Linear regression*

19. Falewicz, J.: Kontrola niezmienności związku korelacyjnego, *Zeszyty Naukowe WSE we Wrocławiu,* No. 1, 1956.
20. Feller, W.: *An Introduction to Probability,* New York, 1950.
21. Fisz, M.: *Rachunek prawdopodobieństwa i statystyka matematyczna,* Warszawa, 1954.
22. Frisch, R.: *Pitfalls in the Statistical Construction of Demand and Supply Curves,* Leipzig, 1933.
23. Gardner, F.: *Profit Management and Control,* New York, 1955.
24. Gliwienko, W.: *Rachunek prawdopodobieństwa,* Warszawa–Wrocław, 1953.
25. Gniedienko, B. W.: *Kurs teorii veroyatnostiej,* Moscow–Leningrad, 1953.
26. Gossen, H. H.: *Entwicklung der Gesetze des menschlichen Verkehrs und der daraus fliessenden Regeln für menschliches Handeln,* third edition, Berlin, 1926.
27. Grenander, U., and Rosenblatt, M.: *Statistical Analysis of Stationary Time Series,* New York, 1957.
28. Hald, A.: *Statistical Theory with Engineering Applications,* New York, 1952.
29. Hellwig, Z.: *Elementy rachunku prawdopodobieństwa i statystyki matematycznej,* Łódź, 1957.
30. Hellwig, Z.: Uwagi i wnioski z zakresu teorii potrzeb, *Zeszyty Naukowe WSE we Wrocławiu,* No. 2, 1957.
31. Hellwig, Z.: Wyznaczanie parametrów regresji liniowej metodą dwóch punktów, *Zastosowania Matematyki* , Vol. 3, 1956.
32. Jagłom, A. M.: Obshchaya teoriya statsyonarnykh swuchaynykh funkcii, *Uspekhi matematicheskikh nauk,* Vol. 7, series 5 (51).
33. Kendall, M. G.: *The Advanced Theory of Statistics,* Vol. 2, London, 1946.
34. Keynes, J. M.: *Ogólna teoria zatrudnienia, procentu i pieniądza,* Warszawa, 1952.
35. Lange, O.: *Teoria statystyki,* Warszawa, 1952.
36. Leontief, W. W.: Ein Versuch zur statistischen Analyse von Angebot und Nachfrage, *Weltwirtschaftliches Archiv,* Vol. 30, 1929.
37. Lyle, P.: *Regression Analysis of Production Costs and Factory Operations,* London, 1946.
38. Marks, K.: *Kapitał,* Vol. 1, Warszawa, 1951.
39. Moore, H. L.: *Economic Cycles: Their Law and Their Cause,* New York, 1914.
40. Nicholson, C.: The Probability Integral for Two Variables, *Biometrika,* 33, 1943.

41. Ostroumow, S. S.: *Sudebnaya statistika*, Moscow, 1949.
42. Pareto, V.: *Cours d'économie politique*, Lausanne, 1896–1897.
43. Paulsen, A.: *Allegemeine Volkswirtschaftslehre*, Band 2, Berlin, 1956.
44. Pearson, K.: *Tables for Biometricians and Statisticians*, London, 1931.
45. Pigou, A. C.: A Method of Determining the Numerical Value of Elasticities of Demand, *Economic Journal*, Vol. 20 (1910), p. 636 ff.
46. Pigou, A. C.: The Statistical Derivation of Demand Curves, *Ekonomic Journal*, Vol. 40 (1930), p. 384 ff.
47. Richter-Altschaffer, H.: *Einführung in die Korrelationsrechnung*, Berlin, 1931.
48. Sadowski, W.: O nieparametrycznym teście na porównywanie rozsiewów, *Zastosowania Matematyki*, Vol. 2, No. 2.
49. Schmalenbach, E.: *Grundlagen der Selbstkostenrechnung und Preispolitik*, Leipzig, 1930.
50. Schultz, H.: *Statistical Laws of Demand and Supply, with Special Application to Sugar*, Chicago, 1928.
51. Schultz, H.: *The Theory and Measurement of Demand*, Chicago, 1938.
52. Sheppard, W. F.: On the Application of the Theory of Error to Cases of Normal Distribution and Normal Correlation, *Phil. Trans. Roy. Soc.* (1998), p. 101.
53. Smith, V. L.: Engineering Data and Statistical Techniques in the Analysis of Production and Technological Change in Fuel Requirements of the Trucking Industry, *Econometrica*, Vol. 25, No. 2, 1957.
54. Stieltjes, T. J.: Extrait d'une lettre adressée à M. Hermite, *Bulletin Scientifique Math.*, series 2, 13 (1889), p. 170.
55. Styś, W.: Złudzenia statystyczne wywołane przez wpływ czasu w badaniach zjawisk demograficznych w ich ruchu i rozwoju, *Przegląd Antropologiczny*, Vol. 23.
56. Tinbergen, J.: *Wprowadzenie do ekonometrii*, Warszawa, 1957.
57. Tintner, G.: *Econometrics*, New York, 1954.
58. Tintner, G.: *Mathematics and Statistics for Economists*, London, 1954.
59. Tschuprow, A. A.: *Principles of the Mathematical Theory of Correlations*, London–Edinburgh–Glasgow, 1939.
60. Wald, A.: The Approximate Determination of Indifference Systems by Means of Engel Curves, *Econometrica*, Vol. 8, 1940.
61. Winkler, W.: *Podstawowe zagadnienia ekonometrii*, Warszawa, 1957.

62. Wold, H.: *A Study in the Analysis of Stationary Time Series,* Uppsala, 1938.
63. Yule, G. M.: On the Theory of Correlation for Any Number of Variables, Treated by a New System of Notation, *Proc. Roy. Soc.,* London, series A 79 (1907).
64. *The USA* (joint work), Chicago, 1957.
65. *Rocznik Statystyczny 1956,* GUS, Warszawa.

LIST OF SUPPLEMENTARY LITERATURE

Anderson, T. W.: *Introduction to Multivariate Statistical Analysis,* New York, 1958.
Bartlett, M. S.: Fitting a Straight Line When Both Variables are Subject to Error, *Biometrika,* 5, 1949.
Ezekiel, M., and Fox, K.: *Methods of Correlation and Regression Analysis,* New York, 1959.
Lange, O.: *Wstęp do ekonometrii,* Warszawa, 1960.
Pawłowski, Z.: *Ekonometryczne metody badania popytu konsumpcyjnego,* Warszawa, 1961.
Wald, A.: The Fitting of Straight Lines if Both Variables are Subject to Error, *Ann. of Math. Statist.,* 11, 3, 284, 1940.
Williams, E. J.: *Regression Analysis,* New York, 1951.